EJECT! EJECT!

Bryan Philpott

LONDON

IAN ALLAN LTD

Contents

First published 1989

ISBN 0 7110 1804 9

© Bryan Philpott 1989

Published by Ian Allan Ltd, Shepperton, Surrey; and printed by Ian Allan Printing Ltd at their works at Coombelands in Runnymede, England

Sole distributors for the USA

Osceola, Wisconsin 54020, USA

Jacket photographs courtesy of Martin-Baker Aircraft Co Ltd

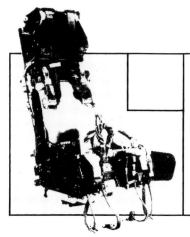

Introduction

It is not my intention that this book should be regarded as either a definitive history or a technical guide to the ejection seat. I set out to outline how the seat has been developed over the years and in so doing found that its history goes back further than perhaps many, other than serious students of aviation, realise.

When teams of engineers set out with a common aim, it is almost certain they will arrive at the same conclusions, albeit by taking many different paths, some of which may have crossed en route. This is very much the case with the design and development of the ejection seat and associated escape capsules. To detail every facet of such work, and every variation, would not only have resulted in a book that would not have been commercially viable, but also probably very repetitive.

I shall be very surprised if my efforts to present an overall picture satisfy everyone. As far as the manufacturers are concerned, it was clearly not possible to detail all the work carried out by each one of them; in certain areas I have had to overcome the problem of overlap and have tried to make this clear where it has happened.

Circumstances dictated that Martin-Baker Aircraft Co Ltd, whose name has become synonymous with ejection seats in many countries, features most prominently, for it was conveniently to hand in England, but this is not in any way intended to deprecate work done by manufacturers in other countries, some of whom went to a great deal of trouble to supply information. Some chose not to reply to letters, others politely declined to supply answers to my questions. In such cases I decided either to mention this in the text or to make no reference whatsoever, rather than be misquoted or resort to guesswork. So there are some gaps, but these were inevitable and do not, in my opinion, affect the overall story that I have tried to present.

As far as individual stories are concerned, I was not able to feature some that I wanted to in the detail I felt necessary. This is due to circumstances ranging from the need to be wary of legal restraints, personal reasons of those involved, lack of confirmation of questionable information and, once again — in most cases — the polite refusal of air forces, individuals and other authorities to release requested details. However, I feel that overall those who did readily agree have enabled me to present a cross-section of stories that support the technical ins and outs.

It has often been said that truth is stranger than fiction. I feel that some of the stories go a long way to support this as well as to underline the rather unique seriousness tempered with much humour that permeates the military aviation world. I should very much have liked to include the full story of the American pilot who had a tyre burst as he took off in a very heavily-loaded OV-10 Bronco. It became apparent that the aircraft was not going to leave the ground; and all his efforts to stop, including the introduction of reverse thrust, failed, so he ejected. He landed quite safely — about 100ft away from where the Bronco had managed to execute a perfect touch-down on all three wheels and with the propellers in reverse. After removing his parachute, the pilot calmly walked over to the undamaged aircraft and shut down both engines!

Maybe this story, and others both serious and dramatic, will be told one day. In the meantime I must accept total responsibility for those used throughout the book, and very much hope that they convey an accurate picture of how the ejection seat has saved many lives.

Bryan Philpott
January 1988

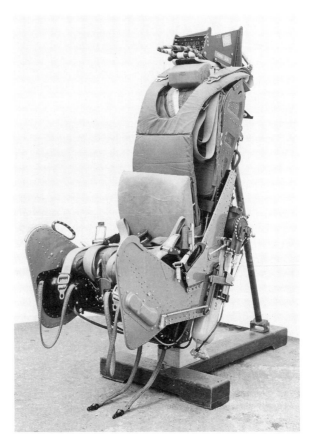

Above:
A Martin-Baker seat designed for underwater ejection as fitted to RN Buccaneer aircraft. The air cylinder is visible. *Martin-Baker*

Acknowledge-ments

Although the final decision as to what to include and what to omit from the mass of material accumulated during research must rest with me, I could not have made such a decision without having received the help and co-operation from many authorities, fellow authors and individuals. I would like to thank them all for their unselfish help and at the same time apologise to any I may have omitted.

It would perhaps be invidious to single out too many for special mention, but I feel that I must express my gratitude to Hans Mennborg of Saab-Scania who made a special journey to discuss his company's products with me, similarly Del Holyland of Martin-Baker, a good friend who came to my rescue when typewriters at Denham seemed to be as unfashionable as conventional aircraft seats, and Sqn Ldr John West (ret'd), who very generously made available to me his own research and several papers he compiled whilst editor of the RAF Support Command's Flight Safety Magazine, and allowed me to quote from them.

Sincere thanks must go to the directors of Martin-Baker for allowing me to use material from their records and publications, including their privately published book, by the late Wg Cdr John Jewell, *Engineering for Life*; to the Ministry of Defence, in particular Wg Cdrs Jerry Witts, Chris Marshall, Mick Marsh and Philip Burden; RAF Strike and Support Commands; Director of Flight Safety RAF; Sqn Ldrs Stephen Griggs and Jeff Glover; and Flt Lt Ken Topaz.

The USAF, in particular the Department of the Air Force Air University Centre for Aerospace Doctrine, Research & Education, Maxwell AFB; Gen Kirk James, Third Air Force; Cols Lonnie Sandford, James Horney and Jim Davies; Lt-Col Edward Neunherz; Majs Earl Tilford Jr, Gary Fullington and Barry Horne; Capt Leslie Fraze; 2nd Lt June Green; Sgt David Malakoff.

The Pressezentrum Der Luftwaffe; Majs Hans-Joachim Zabler and Martin Dötzer; Dr Volker Koos.

The RAF Museum; the Australian War Memorial; the Science Museum; British Aerospace; The Royal Aeronautical Society; Pilot Press Ltd; The *Sunday Express; Aviation News; Aircraft Illustrated; FlyPast; Air Mail; Air Force Times; Flight.*

John Lancaster; Ralph Barker; Richard Leask Ward; Doug Rough; Alan W. Hall; Ken Ellis; Norman Franks; Chaz Bowyer; Graham Carter; Dr Dewi Morgan; Ivan Spring; Gordon Bartley; Lt-Cdr John Eatwell RN (ret'd); Peter Lowe; John Boulter; Bryan Wilburn; Robert Dorr; Charles Reid; Denis Newton;

Charles Sylvester; Charles King; Brian Miller; Ian White; Oddy Rada-Ludlow and Heather Cook, who both kindly did a lot of difficult translation work; Rita Ward who once again toiled through the manuscript picking up all the areas where I had pressed the wrong keys; and all aircrew from a variety of air forces who sent details of their experiences, some of which I have mentioned in detail and others in support of some part of the text.

Technical development in the field will carry on, and ejection seats from many different manufacturers will continue to give military aircrew throughout the world the comfort of knowing that at whatever height, speed and condition they encounter a problem, survival will be a case of 'BANG! . . . You're alive.'

Above:
Pictures of genuine emergency ejections are rare. This one shows test pilot Don Knight ejecting from Lightning XG311 on 31 July 1963. *BAe*

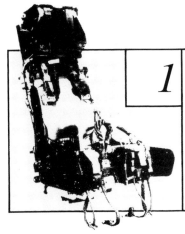

1 Part One
The Means To
An End

The fact that it was Friday the 13th had not even crossed Flt Lt Gray M. Bacon's mind. The cloudless sky formed a blue canopy over the twinkling waters of the Mediterranean, his Vampire T11 was performing well, and beside him sat his AOC, AVM C. D. C. Boyce. Flying from Nicosia with the Middle East Air Force in 1956 was a bonus that Gray Bacon also enjoyed; in fact life all round seemed pretty good. AVM Boyce was a competent and enthusiastic aerobatic pilot, his main experience having been on Meteors, and had asked Flt Lt Bacon to demonstrate the prowess of the Vampire: it was this that Bacon was now doing. Keeping well within the restrictions that were in force on Vampires at that time, Flt Lt Bacon called on all his skills to hurl the tiny aircraft through a personally satisfying sequence that would also impress his AOC. Having accomplished this he handed control to AVM Boyce to enable him to emulate his tutor. As the Vampire rolled off the top of a loop the fire warning light came on. Gray Bacon immediately took control, throttled back, closed the HP cock and pressed the fire extinguisher buttons. Despite all his actions the light stayed on. He advised air traffic of his problem, and decided to abandon the Vampire. Making sure it was heading out to sea, he jettisoned the canopy then called into his intercom the two words that neither he nor AVM Boyce had expected to hear just a few moments before, but which were now part of standard R/T emergency procedure guaranteed to bring instant response from the recipient:

'Eject! Eject!'

At 7,000ft and 180kt IAS, AVM Boyce pulled the face blind of the Martin-Baker Mk 3B and became the first officer of air rank to save his life using an ejection seat. Flt Lt Bacon turned the descending Vampire to enable him to spot the AVM, saw that his parachute was deployed, advised air traffic, then ejected himself. Both men were picked up by helicopter and neither suffered major injuries, although Gray Bacon did damage his back, a not unfamiliar occurrence in early ejections. He later wrote to Martin-Baker:

. . . I really am most grateful for the initiative and effort that you have continually used to give the RAF the safest and speediest way of leaving a modern aircraft . . .

His closing remarks were very apt, for without the ejection seat it is very likely that neither men would have been able to abandon the stricken aircraft. This was the 107th successful ejection using Martin-Baker seats, and some 30 years later the total of lives saved using escape systems of this type is estimated to be close to 10,000. Over 5,600 of these are credited to Martin-Baker, whose name is now synonymous with this piece of safety equipment. But in terms of the history of aviation the ejection seat is not a new invention brought about by the advent of jet-engined aircraft: its origins go back to 1930, just 27 years after the Wright brothers' 'Flyer' took to the air at Kitty Hawk.

It was the development of the parachute, initially issued and used by observation balloon crews in World War 1, and later by German pilots, which paved the way towards a reliable method of escape. The reluctance of the RFC and later RAF hierarchy to issue pilots and observers with the device is well known, but clearly their arguments had no foundation and this vital piece of equipment became a standard part of every airman's inventory. As aircraft speeds increased so too did the problems of abandoning them in the event of an emergency. In the very early days it was merely a matter of climbing out of the cockpit or diving over the wing trailing edge. But this became progressively more difficult and other techniques evolved. During World War 2, piston-engined fighters were reaching speeds at which the slipstream quite often pinned pilots into their cockpits after they had jettisoned the canopy. By trimming the aircraft nose down, it was possible to roll inverted, and by kicking the stick forward, be ejected from the aircraft in the ensuing bunt. This was successful only under very favourable conditions from fighter type aircraft, and quite apart from the speed aspect there were other factors to be taken into account. Interrogation of returning aircrew from PoW camps revealed that at least 20% of those surviving parachute escapes had been seriously impeded by the effects of 'g'. This caused delay in reaching — and in some cases the jamming of — escape hatches, loss of consciousness, injury, disorientation and a variety of other hazards which affected the chance of escape. There were many instances of men trapped in spinning bombers owing their lives to the fact that the aircraft broke up in mid air: in such cases it was not unusual for the escapee not to be able to recall just when and how he had deployed his parachute.

Fire was a general occurrence in aircraft crippled by enemy action, and once again there were instances of crews being trapped and their parachutes severely damaged by fire before they managed to leave the falling aircraft. At speeds up to about 150kt the success rate of unassisted escapes is about 75%, but as speed increases the fall is dramatic, going down to 25% at 200kt and barely 2% at 290kt.

Statistics like these were in the mind of Flg Off A. M. Dudgeon of No 208 Squadron. When the Squadron changed its Bristol Fighters for Armstrong Whitworth Atlases in 1930, he gave serious thought to the problem of getting out of the new aircraft. The Atlas had a top speed of 145mph (knots were not in vogue at that time) and could reach more than 200mph in a dive. Squadron pilots knew that at these speeds leaving the cockpit against the force of the airstream or under 'g' conditions would be very difficult. Dudgeon therefore turned his attention to designing an assisted escape system. His idea was to mount the pilot's seat on concentric sliding tubes, each containing a strong spring. The springs were to be wound down with a key-operated ratchet and held compressed by a catch.

Releasing the catch would cause the springs to uncoil, forcing the seat — and pilot attached to it — upwards into the airstream. The latter was normally the hardest part of an unassisted escape. Having been helped to a position level with the top of the cockpit coaming, it was envisaged that it would be very much easier for the pilot to leave the aircraft by rolling out to port or starboard. Dudgeon submitted drawings and a working model to the Air Ministry (as it then was), but the idea was rejected, one of the arguments being that anything making it easier for the pilot to leave the aircraft in an emergency would not encourage him to try to get the aircraft home — shades of the original case put forward against the issue of parachutes. Whatever the reasons, be they the penalty of additional weight, finance or just general bureaucratic apathy, the intrepid Flg Off's ideas were lost to gather dust in some inner sanctum, and throughout the 1930s and 1940s little thought was given to the subject, at least within the United Kingdom. In Sweden and Germany there was a refreshingly different approach.

Aircraft development in prewar Germany investigated many exciting avenues, some of which were to come to fruition with various degrees of success. One common factor identified by most German designers was that at the speeds they were concerned with, crew escape would only be possible if they were forcibly propelled away from the aircraft's structure either in some form of capsule, or attached to their seats. Attention was turned to what was initially called 'catapult seats'. Work on forced ejection was first started in 1939 when Junkers wished to test thoroughly the manoeuvrability and general handling characteristics of the Ju88. It was felt that the test programme envisaged could well result in some form of structural failure and therefore an ejection seat would give the test pilots a good chance of survival. In the event, although a seat was installed for test flights, it was never used; and apart from later installations in Junkers 88 and 188 night-fighters, it was not fitted to operational versions of the aircraft.

This information was revealed in October 1945 when officers of the RAF's Institute of Aviation Medicine interrogated Dr S. Ruff, who had been Head of the Medical Institute of the DVL in Berlin. During the course of this interrogation several important medical aspects which will be touched on later also came to light. At this stage it is worth noting that Dr Ruff commented that wartime analysis of statistics collected by the Germans showed that in many cases of successful conventional escapes, especially at high speeds, pilots had been killed or suffered major injuries from striking the tail unit. This, according to Dr Ruff, also highlighted the need for some form of ejection seat in 'modern' (sic) aircraft. Much of the German research was carried out on test rigs at Adlershof under the supervision of Dr Ruff, and at the Heinkel works at Rostock under Dr Gertz, who is credited with the development of the cartridge-operated ejection gun. Little has survived in relation to the Junkers seat for which a patent was lodged in 1941, but by all accounts it was fairly primitive and somewhat complicated in operation. Dornier, Heinkel and Focke-Wulf all developed their own design of ejection seats in which either a compressed air system (Heinkel 219, Dornier 335) or explosive cartridges (Focke-Wulf Ta 154, Heinkel 162) were used. Another course of exploration followed by German scientists was ejection of the complete cockpit assembly in the form of an escape module, therefore anticipating by over 20 years that used on the F-111, for example. To put this German research into perspective it is worth examining the state-of-the-art of aircraft development some German manufacturers had reached before and during the war, and the need for ejection seats and/or jettisonable crew capsules.

A paper entitled *Rescue Equipment for the Crews of High Speed Aircraft* was written by Flugkapitän Paul Spremburg and handed to Sqn Ldr John West, who at the time was editor of RAF Support Command's Flight Safety Magazine, and it is quoted verbatim with his kind permission.

'The development of ejection seats became necessary with high speed aircraft, neither a forced landing nor a parachute jump are possible owing to the accelerations involved and the force of the slipstream.

'With speeds above 250mph, the danger arises that the parachute could tear on opening. As Germany was already building, before the Second War War, aircraft whose speeds were reaching over 500mph, special provision had to be made for the safety of the pilot in a possible emergency. In 1938 designers at the Ernst Heinkel Flugzeugwerke at Rostock were already occupied with the construction of the world's first rocket-propelled "liquid fuel" aircraft, the He176. Special provision was made for the safety of the pilot with this radical aircraft. In an emergency not only could the canopy be jettisoned, but the whole cockpit area, to a length of about 5ft, could be separated from the fuselage. The locking mechanism worked on the principle of bayonet fasteners incorporated into three fuselage longerons and which separated the cockpit from the fuselage by compressed air. Flying and engine controls were also disconnected in the same manner.

'An interesting point is that, at first, most normal instruments were not fitted until the tactical employment of the aircraft should have been decided. On the other hand, lengthy research was required to produce the special cockpit hood out of one sheet of Plexiglass. Seemingly endless work was required to remove tiny scratches or unevenness until at last a useable sample was obtained.

'In order to give the pilot sufficient time to bale out successfully after separation of the cockpit module from the fuselage, the cockpit capsule was fitted with a specially designed brake parachute which deployed automatically. Jettison trials on a wooden cockpit apparatus from a He111, however, revealed an unpleasant characteristic. The brake parachute did not always develop properly because in the initial stages of opening it tended to become blown against and moulded to the cockpit capsule. This technical hitch was soon overcome, however, by building in behind the parachute, a rubber cushion connected to a compressed air cylinder. Some 5sec after cockpit/fuselage separation occurred, the compressed air valve automatically opened, the rubber cushion was inflated in fractions of a second and the brake parachute safely impelled into the airstream. After the introduction of this innovation, no further jettison failures were experienced. Now another question arose: was it possible, in the event of a pilot being unconscious or seriously wounded, for the brake parachute to return both the pilot and cockpit to earth undamaged? To answer this question a specimen cockpit was built and fitted with a life-size wooden dummy, the strength of whose joints and limbs roughly corresponded with those of a live person. After successful release, it was deduced that, in an emergency, it might be possible to get away with merely a broken ankle!'

The He176 was the first rocket-powered aircraft in the world and made its maiden flight on 20 June 1939 with Erich Warsitz at the controls. It was a single-seat machine powered by a Walter HWK-R1 203 rocket engine of 1,340lb static thrust which used hydrogen peroxide and methanol as fuel.

The potency of this aircraft was ably demonstrated on 3 July 1939 when Warsitz reached 528mph. However, parallel to these developments came the appearance of the jet engine, one of which, the He-S-3B, was installed in the Heinkel He178 which on 28 August 1939, again in the hands of Warsitz, became the first jet-powered aircraft to fly. Heinkel decided that it would be better to pursue a design with two jet engines so on 20 June 1939 work was started on the He180 and its later derivative the He280, the first twin-engined jet fighter in the world. Both Messerschmitt in Germany with his Me262 and Carter in England with the Gloster Meteor, favoured the twin-jet layout for safety reasons and because of the comparatively low power then available from jet engines, so development by all three pioneers was along very similar lines. One major difference, however, was that from the very beginning the Heinkel He280 incorporated a compressed air-operated ejection seat. The Me262 was later to be fitted with a similar seat, but it was not until late 1949 that the Meteor F Mk 8 with a Martin-Baker cartridge-operated seat followed suit, although the Mk III/IV featured prominently in Martin-Baker's research work.

On 2 April 1941 Fritz Schäfer took the He280 into the air for the first time using power from the twin He-S-8B 1,600lb st turbine engines. This was accomplished with a fuel load sufficient for one circuit, and the landing was carried out with the fuel warning lights blinking at the pilot. The He280 provided a great deal of useful research information into jet flight, but fits into this narrative because on 13 January 1942 the prototype, DL+AS, now at Rechlin and fitted with four Argus As014 pulse jets to aid research into power units for the Fi103 (V1 flying bomb), was involved in a major incident.

Power from the pulse jets was insufficient to enable the aircraft to carry out a conventional take-off, and it was therefore towed into the air by a pair of Bf110C tugs. The weather was very bad at the time and soon after take-off a heavy snow-storm was encountered. The He280 began to ice up so at an altitude of 7,875ft, finding that he had virtually no control, test pilot Schenk jettisoned the canopy and fired his ejection seat, thus becoming the first man to save his life in an emergency with such a safety device. It is believed that the seat developed by Heinkel and used by Schenk was proved and tested by a parachutist named Busch, both on the test rig at Heinkel and from an aircraft, so to him must go the credit of being the first man to use an ejection seat, but Schenk is certainly the first recorded user under emergency conditions. Schenk's seat was a standard one to which was attached the ejection gun, in this case a compressed air cylinder and its associated refinements, enabling it to exit the aircraft cleanly. Later this very rudimentary design was improved by the fitting of more substantial guidance rails, and cushioning, but it was not until 1943 in live tests on a new inclined ramp at Rostock that Heinkel began to produce a much improved version for installation in the He219 night-fighter. From late 1942 all new design high-speed fighter and fighter-bomber aircraft were provided with some form of ejection seat: the Me309 was used for experimental work on ejection seats that were eventually to be fitted to operational Me262s, the Heinkel 219 as well as the Arado 234 (the first twin-jet powered bomber in the world and believed to be the first aircraft to be equipped with a landing braking parachute) were also equipped with such seats, and so were the unconventional Dornier Do335 and the DFS228 rocket-powered reconnaissance aircraft.

Following Schenk's successful escape in 1942 the work at Heinkel's experimental establishment tended to move more towards the use of a cartridge-operated ejection gun in favour of the compressed air version. On the test ramp at Rostock an ejection velocity of 32ft/sec with a peak 'g' of 14 was reached. It was also discovered that attention to what might seem like minor points, such as lubrication of the guide rails, enabled a slightly higher velocity to be achieved. This of course applied whatever the power source.

In the Heinkel He219 the pilot and observer seats were fixed back-to-back. Located in the nosewheel bay were four 2-litre bottles of compressed air, two on the starboard side operating the pilot's seat and two on the port for the observer's. Quick release valves directed compressed air to the bottom of the pistons in the respective seat cylinders (ejection guns — to give some idea of size, the pistons had a stroke of 69cm and a diameter of 9cm). Five volunteers made 14 launches in tests at three different bottle pressures of 880lb/sq in, 1,350lb/sq in and 1,550lb/sq in. The guinea pigs all reported some discomfort and back pain at the higher pressure level.

Dr Ruff commented that investigation into injection seats was conducted along similar lines to that taking place in Sweden and England. He commented that minimum ejection velocity was calculated for each aircraft and the figures confirmed by wind tunnel tests. Calculations were also proved by ground testing, dummy ejections and finally live tests carried out by volunteer parachutists. Many of the test shots were carried out from Heinkel He219 DH+PV.

Although Dornier and Focke-Wulf each developed their own type of seat, co-operation was such that they eventually dispensed with compressed air-activated seats and concentrated on the cartridge-operated one for which Gertz at Rostock had developed the most efficient gun. Cartridges for this were manufactured at Eisfeld near Holle and an initial order for 500 had been placed when the war ended.

By this time the value of the system had been ably demonstrated and over 60 Luftwaffe aircrew owed their lives to the compressed air ejection seat, the distinction of being the first to use it in combat going to Unteroffizer Herter and Gefreiter Perbix of 2NJG1 on 11 April 1944 when they ejected from a Heinkel He219.

Meanwhile, by early 1944 Focke-Wulf was obtaining slightly better results than Heinkel. By using only initial guidance in the acceleration path the company reduced friction produced by full-length guide rails, and its cartridge-activated seat achieved 36ft/sec and a peak acceleration of 18g. The FW seat was intended for installation in the Kurt Tank-designed Ta154, a machine that was to have been the Luftwaffe's answer to the superlative de Havilland Mosquito. It was a high-wing twin-piston-engined all-weather/night-fighter, which like the Mosquito was constructed mainly of wood. Inadequacies in available glue resulted in the aircraft breaking up in flight and it never entered service. Trial installations of the FW seat were made in the FW190, but it is not known if it was ever used in emergency situations.

The need to clear high fins, mentioned by Dr Ruff, was reflected by Dornier's approach to the ejection seat, for that company's design not only needed to throw the occupant above the fin but also to clear the rear propeller of its unusual Dornier Do335 aircraft. As a feasibility study in driving a rear pusher propeller by a long extension shaft through the fuselage, Schempp-Hirth built the Gö9 experimental aircraft (D-EBVW). Dornier adopted the concept for its Do335 Pfiel (Arrow) fighter, which was powered by two 12-cylinder 1,900hp Daimler Benz DB603G engines driving both pusher and tractor propellers. The pilot, and in the A-6 night-fighter version the radar operator, had ejection seats the development of which was influenced by the need to clear the fin and rear propeller. To do this with any certainty of success an ejection velocity of 57.4ft/sec would be needed, and this was higher than the Heinkel or FW seats could attain.

On production aircraft, to reduce the ejection velocity needed to clear the rear of the aircraft, arrangements were made to blow off the fin and rear propeller: by doing this, the velocity required to clear the tail by 3ft fell to 44.6ft/sec, which was thought to be tolerable. This modification meant that the seat was finally given a mean acceleration of $12\frac{1}{2}$g over $\frac{1}{7}$sec with a peak of 25g being reached $\frac{1}{50}$sec after the start of the stroke. This rate of onset of acceleration, or in aviation medicine terms 'jolt', of 1,250g/sec, is far beyond what would be tolerable today.

All the tests were observed and separate reports on specialist aspects of them produced by scientists from Dornier, Heinkel, the DVL Berlin, and Rechlin; and it is quite clear from some of them that a great deal of discomfort was experienced by the volunteer ejectees. At the time it was thought that the provision of arm-rests to take some of the weight, plus cushioning and general padding of the seat, would limit the discomfort, and it is clear that the need to limit both peak acceleration and velocity, the phenomena of jolt and overshoot was not properly understood. Independently, the late Sir James Martin quickly realised that these were the crucial physiological factors governing ejection, as we shall see later on.

The Dornier seat was a direct development of the Heinkel design, but because of the far greater ejection velocity needed, three instead of two 2-litre compressed air bottles were needed, and the piston stroke was increased to 100cm. Dornier Report No 3240 on the trials conducted at Friedrichshafen gives interesting details of the results of firing 10 volunteers, ages 21 to 34 and weighing from 145lb to 175lb, at bottle pressures from 880lb/sq in to 2,000lb/sq in. The seat was fired at 77° from the horizontal and caught in a wire mesh net which was suspended from posts by elastic cord. To help absorb the impact of the seat's arrival, the net was covered with wood shavings.

The emphasis on any escape is speed, so instantaneous decisions are vital. (There is the archetypal story of the student pilot about to fly in a Vampire T11 and encounter the ejection seat for the first time, to whom the instructor said. 'If I tell you to eject, don't say what? or you will be talking to yourself!') The drill for ejection from the Do335 could hardly be called speedy, and is therefore worth looking at since it makes interesting comparison with modern procedures.

Three switches on the cockpit starboard side panel had to be depressed in sequence before ejection could be attempted. The sequence was as follows:

i.   First switch — blow off rear propeller.
ii.   Second switch — blow off upper tail fin.

iii. Third switch — arm the ejection seat (this removed a lock from the piston).
iv. Jettison the hood manually; and finally . . .
v. Squeeze the trigger on the arm rest to fire the seat.

Clearly this is not the simple one-action operation of modern seats, and as no figures seem to have survived it is not possible to ascertain what limits would have been involved. It is obvious that the decision to eject would have been taken at some height to be sure of success.

After the war, results of German tests as well as examples of seats became available to the Allies, and these were studied in great depth. There can be little doubt that much useful data was obtained. Prewar American studies of the possibility of ejection had led nowhere, but the importance of the development of this type of safety equipment led on 23 January 1941 to the forming of a committee at Wright Field to study safe egress from aircraft with pusher propellers. In 1944 research was expanded to include all modern types of high-speed aircraft; this taking on new importance in 1945 when two Curtiss P-55s crashed while performing low-altitude manoeuvres, and both pilots failed to escape. This and the knowledge of German use of ejection seats in operational aircraft was a spur to the Americans, who at that time were looking at methods of downward ejection, a system developed and used in the B-47. An account of early tests of this installation appears later.

Acquisition of German seats in May 1945 was a great stimulus, and one from a Heinkel He162 was fitted into P-80A 42-84995 in August of that year. All efforts to make it fire safely failed, so work started on the redesign of the basic German seat, and by February 1946 a P-61 appropriately named 'Jack-in-the-Box' (42-39498) had been fitted out as a test aircraft.

Both the British and the Americans, who were to become the leaders in jet-powered aircraft design in the immediate postwar years, had to a degree lagged behind Germany and Sweden as far as practical wartime investigation into ejection seats was concerned. Almost parallel to the German efforts were those in Sweden of Saab, a company established in 1937 by a group of industrialists to produce aircraft for the Swedish Government. Initially and in order to obtain experience, the company produced under licence a quantity of Junkers Ju86K bombers and Northrop 8A-1 (B5) light fighter-bombers. (The fact that the two aircraft built under the licence agreement were German and American is coincidental rather than an expression of Sweden's declared neutrality, but bearing in mind the political situation in Europe in 1937/38, the acquisition of plans for the German bomber does say a great deal for the skill of the Swedish negotiators!) Throughout its history Saab has demonstrated a unique ability to produce not only very advanced aircraft but also ancillary equipment. Much of the groundwork came in the dark days of 1939-45, when war, so often the mother of invention, did not provide the spur to the Swedes that it did to the combatant nations: during this time they developed a very advanced 'toss' bomb-sight, as well as operational ejection seats.

After the war Saab continued to develop support equipment and its ejection seat, as well as diversifying. Today there are three main areas of operation, aircraft (including missiles), electronics and automotive. In the aeronautical field,

14

the company plays a leading role in Western Europe in the development of advanced military aircraft, and although they are now using Martin-Baker seats on new designs, their own equipment is still very much in service.

Saab's escape studies started in 1940 with development of the Mk 1 seat, culminating in test ejections of a dummy from a modified Saab B17. The first was on 8 January 1942 and is believed to be the first air ejection ever recorded. The Saab seat was primarily designed for use in the J21A, a twin-boom fighter with a pusher propeller, so like Dornier the designers were faced with the problem of clearing the rear propeller. Saab chose to use cartridges to fire the seat and this method proved successful enough for the company to retain it for use on all future designs. The first seat went into production in 1943 and was fitted to the J21, unique in that it was later modified to take a jet engine and thus became the only fighter to have been in front-line service in both piston and jet form.

The piston-engined version of the J21 and its ejection seat hit the headlines in Sweden in 1946 when a Gothenberg newspaper carried the headline *Charge under seat delivered pilot from Certain Death*. The report went on to claim for Sweden the first emergency ejection, following a collision at 10,000ft between two aircraft. At the time German successes in this field (including Schenk's ejection) had not come to light; nevertheless Saab's success is notable and, in the absence of any first-hand accounts by German World War 2 escapees, the description of this first escape by the pilot concerned neatly concludes the account of early experimental work aimed at finding a means to an end.

The ejection was reported in the newspapers, and has subsequently been mentioned in other publications, as occurring on 27 July 1946. According to records made available to the author by Saab, and confirmed by the Swedish Air Force, the date was 29 July. Some published accounts in Sweden also name the pilot as Lt Johanson whereas in other documents reference is made to Lt Bengt Järkenstedt. The names do in fact refer to the same man! Bengt Järkenstedt has confirmed that in 1954 he changed his name to the latter. This is his story as written for a RAF Support Command publication in 1981 and translated by Duncan Read:

'The Fighter Wing of Save near Gothenburg in Sweden exercised together with the Swedish Navy at sea northwest of the air base. I myself belonged to the 2nd squadron, for a couple of months equipped with the J21-A1, an aeroplane with a pusher propeller and called "tvestjarten" (Swedish for earwig, the twintail insect). The two remaining squadrons still flew the J22. Our task was to train for attacks on the destroyers with our automatic guns.

'As the weather was fair the tactics were for our first attack to begin from a height of 15,000ft, in flights of three and with the sun in our backs to reduce the effectiveness of the warships' anti-aircraft guns. After the attack we had to climb steeply, turn and then direct new attacks circling down towards the target.

'On the first flight after lunch I was ordered to fly as blue seven; because of engine failures the flight was reduced to a section. I joined my flight commander and was his number two. We took off from the airfield of Save heading southwest climbing out over the sea. The Navy was reported to be about 15 miles off the coast. When we had reached height (15,000ft) and were far enough off the coast, we turned right, to head north. Visibility below us was reduced by some haze, but we soon discovered our target and dived with maximum speed towards a destroyer. I flew in attack formation about 30yd behind and a little to the right of my section leader. After the first attack we made a climbing run to the left with noses up in order to get into position to attack again.

'Suddenly, without warning, my aeroplane shook from a strong thrust and began to move violently. I was sometimes exposed to positive and sometimes to negative "g" and it made me thoroughly shaken. Soon I realised I had come into collision with another aeroplane. At the same time, I sensed that a shadow had rapidly swept by to the left. I dropped my grasp of the control column and when I got hold of it again I felt that the elevator didn't work at all. The stick felt quite loose and the rudder pedals felt just the same. The ailerons, on the contrary, seemed to work and by handling them and the engine which was still running, the plane was gradually stabilised in a flat spin with the nose roughly in a cruising position. The altitude was a good 6,000ft, the air speed indicator wasn't registering and my radio set did not work. I found that the left twintail was torn off from the trailing edge of the wing and realised that the tail plane with the elevator must be missing.

'The engine was still running well but the aeroplane wanted to stay in the spin and was rapidly losing height. The only thing to do was to leave the aeroplane. I didn't feel any hesitation about baling out. In our squadron we had carefully drilled the emergency instructions of the "meat-mincer" (nickname of the J21) and I followed it instinctively without any trouble. My oxyen mask was already in place, I pulled down my flying goggles and pulled the emergency release handle of the cockpit hood. The canopy blew away but the door on my right had to be pushed hard to fall out. Now it was rather windy in the cockpit, but I had to go on.

'I raised my feet into the stirrups, placed my knees together — no trouble — the stick could be placed in forward position, straightened my back with head straight above. I placed my left hand on left knee and grasped with my right hand the ejection seat release handle. I shut my eyes and pulled the handle to my chest . . . Maybe I lost consciousness for a moment, but when I opened my eyes again I found myself falling free from the ejection seat about 30ft above the aeroplane. I thought I would fall on to it again and in order not to do so, quickly pulled my parachute ripcord. The opening was normal; and I was falling flat in the air, face downwards, when the parachute opened.

'Suddenly it became quiet. I could still hear the engine of my plane and saw it bank and rotating, disappear down to the surface of the sea. I made myself comfortable in my parachute harness and felt rather pleased with the situation. After a short while I saw another parachute half a mile off and at a lower height and wondered if he who hung there felt as well as I did. But nothing ever stays quiet for long.

'All at once lots of J21s and J22s were humming around me. They were just about scaring the life out of me. I was afraid of their flying into me so shook my fists at them. The more I shook the more they waved their wings. One was especially intrusive, it came time and again straight at me and passed so close I thought it would blow my parachute into pieces. (Later when I accused the pilot of attempting murder, he embarrassingly excused himself on the grounds that he wanted a good motion picture of me! I am sorry to say he had already used up all the film before he lined up on me.) Gradually things calmed down when they saw I was alive.

'The descent took about 7min. From the first feeling of not moving, the surface of the sea soon began to approach. I noticed the fact that many ships were on the way towards my landing position. I had a life-jacket and raft. The water was agreeably warm and I had trained for a parachute descent with a released canopy from a boat. It ought to turn out all right; it did, but I also took the opportunity to set up my private record in high diving. In our instructions how to land with a parachute in water we were recommended to release from the parachute harness before touch-down on the surface. This was to reduce the risk of becoming tangled in the shroud lines and dragged down into the water by the canopy. Already at a height of about 300ft I released the breast and leg-straps and sat openly in the harness and made up my mind to leave the parachute about 6ft above the surface of the water. This surface, that earlier had seemed so smooth and distant, now began to rush towards me. As a matter of fact I misjudged the height and, as I am told, left the harness at a height of more than 50ft. Such a high dive I had never done either before or since.

'I landed with my back just between two waves in the rather rough sea with a big splash. Before landing I had released one of the two carbon dioxide containers of my life-jacket and I came quickly up to the surface. The hard contact with the water had helped me to release the life-raft from its case and it was comfortably floating up to me ready to be inflated. When I had settled down in the dinghy it was time for the next shock. Fifty yards away I saw a big ship's prow with a high bow wave rushing straight towards me and it seemed as if it would drown me in a few seconds. But it was me they wanted and in a short while I was taken safely on board the destroyer *Sundsvall*.

'The other pilot who shared my misfortune had been taken on board another destroyer and he was also safe. He had been flying as number four in a J22 Flight, diving at ship targets when we came into collision. He lost half of his right wing and his aeroplane also became uncontrollable, so he baled out manually. Together we were taken to a hospital in Gothenburg for a medical examination. They examined my back especially closely to see if I had suffered from the ejection. I hadn't, my only mark being a small bruise on my right elbow. Two days later I was permitted to fly again.'

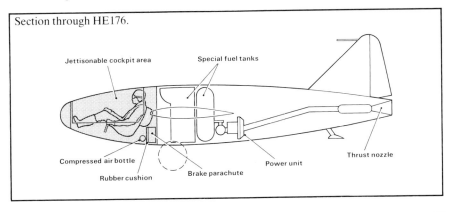

Section through HE176.

Jettisonable cockpit area Special fuel tanks

Compressed air bottle

Rubber cushion Brake parachute Power unit Thrust nozzle

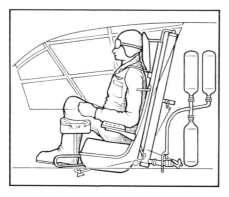

Above:
Pilot's seat arrangement of Do335A.

Above right:
A wartime Heinkel test rig with seat loaded with weights to represent pilot. The glass-fronted box contains an acceleration meter, and the lever with weight is a brake. To the left can be seen another seat. *Dr Volker Koos*

Below:
An early Heinkel seat under test in 1940. The framework around the top is a device to measure acceleration. Note that the occupant is sitting on a parachute pack. *Dr Volker Koos*

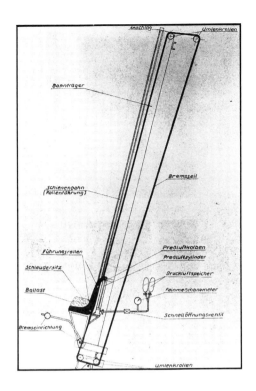

Above:
A 1940 schematic of the Heinkel test rig. *Dr Volker Koos*

Below:
A Saab J21 of the type from which Lt Jägenstedt ejected on 29 July 1946. *Saab*

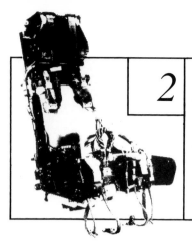

2 Post-War Progress

The pioneering work carried out in Germany and Sweden was revealed after the cessation of hostilities in 1945. By that time it had also of course become very apparent to the Air Staff in England that there was clearly an increasing need for some form of assisted escape system for aircrew, and it was natural that they should turn to James (later Sir James) Martin, the founder of the Martin-Baker Aircraft Co. James Martin, a tough dynamic Ulsterman with an alert inventive mind, left his native shores in his early twenties with just £10 in his pocket to seek his fortune in London. His major ambition was to form his own company, and his determination and frugal living enabled him to acquire premises in Acton from where his remarkable gifts in design and engineering enabled him to manufacture and market a variety of saleable machines including small oil engines and specialised vehicles. In those days he was the inventor, designer, experimental engineer, toolmaker, fitter, assemblyman, salesman and delivery man. On one occasion he designed and made a special type of truck for a customer in Manchester and drove through the night to deliver it to save the expense of hiring a driver. In 1929 he found a site in Denham to expand his business, which he dearly wished to extend to aeroplanes that were to be simpler, safer, cheaper, easy to produce and, above all, easier to fly than others of the period. His first venture into the field came to an end because of limited available finance, but aid from a business friend who had an interest in aviation enabled the Martin Aircraft Works, as the company was then called, to turn to the design of a small, cheap two-seater with a simple but very ingenious method of construction using thin-gauge steel tubing.

In 1934 Capt Valentine Baker, a well known flying instructor and World War 1 fighter pilot, whom James Martin had first met in 1932, joined the team at Denham. He did for the company in the air what James Martin did in the workshop and on the drawing board, and a new company known as the Martin-Baker Aircraft Co Ltd was formed. Its aircraft designs (which used the prefix MB) became well known in the industry, although they did not receive the support they deserved from official procurement sources. The MB3, powered by a Napier Sabre 24-cylinder H-type engine and armed with six cannons, was one of the outstanding designs of the war and could have been developed into a first-rate fighter. On 12 September 1942 it was lost in a crash soon after take-off which not only wrote off the aircraft but also killed Valentine Baker. The double loss was a bitter blow to James Martin who had formed a deep affection and admiration for

20

Baker, and it has been stated that the death of his friend in these circumstances formed the foundation of his interest in aircrew survival from which emanated the now world-famous ejection seat and associated equipment manufactured by Martin-Baker. During the war the company designed and produced cutters which were inserted into aircraft wings to cut cables supporting barrage balloons, ammunition belt feed mechanisms and cockpit canopy jettison equipment.

During the Battle of Britain, the urgent need for a quickly jettisonable cockpit canopy became very apparent. The task of design was entrusted to James Martin whose brief included the need for the retrofitting of equipment to existing aircraft. The outcome was a simple method of unlocking pins actuated by cables, operated by the pilot pulling a small red ball mounted in the cockpit framework. Pulling on the cables unfastened the hood from the fuselage, and the slipstream did the rest. A trial installation was air tested by Wg Cdr D. O. Findlay. Such was the success of this simple device that it was installed as standard on all production Spitfires and those already in service. The company's early foray into this small but important part of escape equipment, developed into a major interest and has continued in parallel to that of ejection seat design.

With the background described (albeit very briefly) it is not too surprising that following the loss of Sqn Ldr W. D. B. S. Davie in a Gloster F9/40 on 4 January 1944 the Air Staff should approach James Martin to look into the design of an escape system that ejected the pilot from the aircraft. Sqn Ldr Davie, who on 30 July 1943 had become the first man in England to bale out of a jet-powered aircraft when he abandoned a Gloster E28/39 at 30,000ft, managed to extract himself from the F9/40 (Meteor prototype) but struck the tail and made no attempt to open his parachute. This highlighted the need for some form of assisted escape as it was clear from the crash investigation that although the unfortunate Davie had managed to get out of the cockpit by diving over the side in the recommended conventional manner, he was thrown into the aircraft's tailplane structure.

At this point it is perhaps worth looking at a simple definition of 'g' forces and the medical problems that James Martin (as well as German and Swedish designers, unknown to him at the time) was meeting. Acceleration is measured in 'g', units of gravity. For example, if you weigh 160lb normally and carry out a manoeuvre in which you pull 6g you will for that time weigh 6×160lb — 960lb. To put this into true perspective it is also necessary to look at the definition of mass. This is the amount of matter in the body and is always the same for that body anywhere in the universe. All bodies with mass attract each other and the force of attraction depends on two things: how close they are and how massive each body is. Thus the closer the bodies, the greater the attraction, such that if you halve the distance between them, you quadruple the force of attraction. Also, the more massive they are, the greater the mutual attraction. In other words the force is proportional to the mass and inversely proportional to the square of the distance between them.

Gravity is the name given to the force of the attraction exerted on something by the earth and weight is the measurement of that force. Therefore weight can vary, depending on how far the body is from the centre of the earth. For example, a person weighs more at sea level than on the top of a mountain — weight becomes progressively less, but mass remains constant. On the surface of the earth we are all subject to 1g or 1 unit of gravity. If we accelerate by changing direction or speed, we measure the accelerative force in further units of gravity. This increased weight affects all parts of the body and is felt whenever there is a change in velocity, this being defined as a change in either speed or direction. Thus acceleration is the rate of change of velocity. When 'g' forces are exerted for prolonged periods of several seconds or more, the effects of acceleration are felt chiefly on the blood. Most readers will be familiar with accelerations which act for a relatively long time — examples being coming to rest in a fast-moving elevator or car, rotating in a big wheel at the fairground, or even pulling 'g' during aerobatics. The factors mainly involved in such situations are the magnitude of the force, its duration and its direction of application in relation to the long axis of the body. Since acceleration has the effect of increasing the apparent weight of the blood, the circulation is put under strain and this leads to the symptoms noted in aircraft manoeuvring. Positive, head-to-foot pressures force the blood from the head towards the feet causing black-outs. Negative, foot-to-head pressures drive the blood to the head and cause red-outs. Chest-to-back, transverse pressures drive the blood the shorter distance across the body which allows much higher pressures of the order of 40g or more to be tolerated. However, abrupt accelerations, lasting only for fractions of a second, are subject to different considerations, the limits being set by the mechanical strength of structures in the body. In ejection it is the spine, together with the pelvis and hips, which are the structures whose strength is of the greatest importance.

The adult spine is a collection of 26 articulated bones or vertebral bodies held together by ligaments and kept upright by muscles. At the top rides the head, while at the bottom, the spinal column is anchored in the pelvis. The top group of bones are the cervical vertebrae numbered from C1 (the atlas) and C2 (the axis) at the top, down to C7. There are then 12 thoracic, or dorsal, vertebrae, numbered T1 to T12, followed by the lumbar vertebrae, L1 to L5. The last nine vertebrae form fused structures, the first five the sacrum, and the final four the coccyx.

The vertebrae are separated by cartilaginous intervertebral discs reinforced by a system of ligaments. It is these discs which sustain most of the compressive forces of ejection. Each one comprises two parts — a nucleus composed of an oval gelatinous mass which, depending on age, contains from 90% to 75% water, and the surrounding annulus which is composed mainly of fibres attached to the vertebral bodies. By its construction the disc offers little resistance to minor forces, but as force increases it becomes more rigid and stable. Compressive or other forces are absorbed and dispersed by displacement of the nucleus and the fibrous ring (annulus) and by disc fluid being forced through small pores in adjacent vertebrae. The whole complex of intervertebral discs, ligaments and muscles acts together as a system of springs and dampers to absorb and distribute normal shocks. Too rapid a rate of disc compression in the spine can overwhelm the discs' ability to dissipate the applied force and can lead to fracture of the vertebral bodies.

During early German experiments it was realised that there is a limit to the amount of 'g' the human frame can withstand. Their findings as to peak 'g' and maximum ejection velocity the body could take were similar and perhaps even a little more cautious, than the conclusions reached much later on by James Martin.

What the German researchers did not fully appreciate was the significance of the rate at which the acceleration of ejection is applied. This rate of application of 'g' is referred to as 'jolt', and quite a small and seemingly easily tolerable 'g' can prove unacceptable to the human frame if achieved in too short a period of time. For instance, if a peak figure of only 10g is reached in $\frac{1}{80}$sec, the body is undergoing a rate of application or jolt of 800g/sec.

The early Heinkel seat designed for the He280 Mk VI, and used by Schenk and from which those used by He219 crews was developed achieved a maximum ejection velocity of 28.5ft/sec, with a peak thrust of between 11g and 12g held for a duration of 0.13sec. Records of gas pressure developed in the ejection gun show that the peak force was reached within the first $\frac{1}{100}$sec. Although 11 to 12g lies well within the limit of human tolerance, the consequent jolt of between 1,100 and 1,200g/sec would now be considered exceptional and an unacceptable hazard.

In 1940 Richter of Heinkel studied tolerance to accelerations lasting between 0.1sec and 0.2sec, the peak being increased in successive trials to from 2.2g to 15g. The limiting factors in these experiments was determined solely by the onset of chest pain and neck stiffness. It was not until 1944 that tests carried out under the supervision of Dr Wiesehofer of DVL, suggested that tolerance to acceleration of short duration was most dependent on the rate of rise of acceleration and that jolt was probably the most important factor in producing injuries. James Martin and other British scientists, particularly those of the Institute of Aviation Medicine, were much quicker to appreciate the need for setting limits to jolt in addition to those set for ejection velocity and peak 'g'. In 1944 when James Martin started investigating methods of ejection, it was felt that any design would have to be applicable to fighter aircraft already in existence, so first thoughts were for a device that could easily be fitted in retrospect. The result was a swinging arm mounted on top of the fuselage, with its rear end on a pivot just forward of the fin and the front provided with U-shaped clips engaging the pilot's parachute harness. A powerful spring was released to swing the arm upwards lifting the pilot from his seat and tossing him clear of the aircraft. At this point the medical limitations as outlined were not uppermost in the designer's mind. On 11 October 1944 a model of the device was constructed and demonstrated to Sir Stafford Cripps who was Minister of Aircraft Production, and ACM Sir Wilfred Freeman, his Chief Executive. Both men showed keen interest and expressed their anxiety to assist. This assistance materialised with the loan of a Defiant aircraft (DR944). Perhaps fortunately, the swinging arm method was not pursued as it was decided that retrospective fitting was not a prime requirement.

Martin and his team turned their attention to an ejectionable seat that would leave the aircraft with the pilot attached to it. In England at that time there was no information available on what the human frame could withstand in the form of upward compressive thrust. Some data relating to the lower 'g' forces applied horizontally in catapult launching of aircraft was available, but clearly this was not applicable to solving the new problem. It was therefore necessary to build a rig to determine the amount of upward 'g' force the human frame could tolerate. The idea was conceived of loading a seat to represent the weight of an occupant, then shooting it up a near vertical path, and measuring the accelerations and rates of 'g' involved. A similar line of experimentation had been carried out in Germany and Sweden both with towers and an unusual rig by Saab. This comprised two cables which were attached to the seat and the volunteer occupant, and were passed over pulleys about 23ft above the seat, the loose ends held by test personnel. When the seat was fired, the people holding the cables ran back hauling in the slack to hold the seat and occupant at the apogee, before lowering both to terra firma. This was used successfully in 1942 to test the early Saab compressed air seat and in 1943 when they switched to an explosive charge. Saab was active throughout the whole period of World War 2 in not only the design of ejection seats but also as the only company to develop and manufacture home-grown combat aircraft for the Swedish Air Force, all of which, where necessary, were fitted with their own ejection seats. This policy has only recently changed with the introduction of some Martin-Baker seats.

Saab's development work followed similar lines to the postwar work of James Martin and was carried out in close co-operation with the equivalent of the Institute of Aviation Medicine (FMV). A seat track with a gradient of 60° to the ground and a height of 13m was built within Saab's factory grounds for tests with the seat that was to be used in the J29. This was later replaced by a 30m rig which is still in use today. The company also modified a Dodge three-axle truck by shortening the frame and removing the springs. A platform was placed behind the cab on which was mounted the test rig. The truck was equipped with a firing device as well as measuring systems and a communications radio. Ejection tests were carried out at speeds of up to 150km/hr on Saab's airfield and the vehicle was still in use when the rocket seat for the J35 (Draken) was developed. Like Martin-Baker in England, Saab used several aircraft for air firing, the first being the Junkers 86 (Saab Type B3) from which the very first seat was fired, the Saab B17 and the Type 32 (Lansen, which proved to be an ideal test platform). The first Swedish patent granted to Saab for the ejection seat was on 17 October 1941, since when it has also patented the following design solutions to particular problems:

(a) arm, leg and head restraints
(b) leg restraints
(c) rocket engine
(d) rocket engine ignition
(e) life vest inflation device
(f) arm restraint system

In late 1944 a 16ft test rig was constructed at Denham, this taking the form of a tripod with one of the legs forming the guide rails; the seat was fired up these by a gun consisting of two telescopic tubes energised by an explosive cartridge. The guide rails were fitted with ratchet stops every 3in so that the seat was arrested at the top of its travel. The first dummy shot with the seat loaded to 200lb was made on 20 January 1945, and four days later one of Martin-Baker's experimental fitters — Bernard Lynch — undertook the first of his many rides. On this noteworthy occasion he was shot by a single charge explosive to a height of 4ft 8in, the mean acceleration being a modest $3\frac{1}{2}$g. In three further tests, the power of the cartridge was increased until a height of 10ft was reached, at which stage he reported the onset of considerable discomfort.

Reports of the experiments at Martin-Baker spread fairly quickly, and there were many who were eager to see and maybe even experience a ride on the test rig. Among those anxious to see this new development was Charles Andrews, a journalist from the *Aeroplane* magazine. He visited Denham and made ride No 14 which resulted in him being the first man in England to suffer significant injury, the nature of which more or less determined the whole path of future development. After being propelled to a height of 10ft, Mr Andrews complained of severe back pains. The mean acceleration had been 4g, however the peak 'g' during the ascent was reached so rapidly that the unfortunate journalist suffered a rate of application of nearly 800g/sec, which resulted in a crushed spinal vertebrae.

James Martin was naturally very concerned to hear of the discomfort experienced by Mr Andrews and was shocked the following day when he telephoned to enquire how he was, only to be told that the writer was in hospital with a broken back! Martin quickly realised that there was something amiss with the theory of ejection as it was then being applied. He puzzled as to how a thrust of 4g could produce such devastating results, and decided to take a close look at the sequence of events following the firing of the cartridge. Study of a high-speed film produced the answer, which was the speed at which the peak 'g' had been reached. It was this event that was mainly responsible for prompting James Martin to take a close look at the structure, strength, and limitations of the human spine.

A surgeon friend, Miss M. Louden, arranged for the inventor to witness several spinal operations, as well as to acquire a human spine on which he could carry out mechanical tests. Martin quickly realised that a jolt was a particularly important factor in short term acceleration, and that the rate of rise of acceleration on the test rig of between 600g/sec and 800g/sec was far too high: there would always be the possibility of spinal injury (especially if ejection occurred with a poor posture position) unless it could be reduced. From these studies he determined the limits which became universally accepted as the definitive criteria for design and construction of ejection seats. His conclusions were that injury to the spine should not happen if the following conditions were fulfilled:

1. The peak acceleration should not exceed 21g and this peak should not be maintained for longer than about $\frac{1}{10}$sec.
2. The onset, or rate of rise of 'g', should not be greater than 300g/sec.
3. In sustaining this acceleration, the body should be held in a position to ensure that adjacent vertebrae are square to each other.

Alterations were carried out to the test seat so that it met the new criteria. To smooth out the acceleration/time curve and achieve objectives 1 and 2, a two-cartridge gun was designed. In this the first cartridge started the seat rising smoothly, and the second one, which was activated by the flame from the first when it was uncovered by a moving piston, boosted the seat further and gradually built up the pressure to the maximum needed. To enable the ejectee to adopt a correct posture, foot rests were provided to push the buttocks into the seat, and activation of the ejection sequence was by a firing handle placed above the occupant's head. This handle was attached to a screen and when it was pulled forwards and downwards, a blind completely covered the ejectee's face. There were two advantages to this. First, the occupant, in reaching up for the handle, automatically assumed the correct posture by straightening his back and squaring up his spinal vertebrae, and secondly, the blind gave some protection to the face from the air blast as the seat left the aircraft. Tests indicated that the new approach was the correct one, and thus the need to try a live ejection drew close. But in addition to jolt there was a further important physical factor that had to be considered — acceleration overshoot.

As we have already seen, the limit of human tolerance to the acceleration forces during ejection is set mainly by the spine. It may be thought that the acceleration of the body would be basically the same as that of the seat, but transmission of the force from seat to hip is affected by any intervening compressible material, such as the seat pack, cushion or even the occupant's own flesh in the form of the buttocks and thighs. During the initial moments of ejection as the seat commences its ascent, these structures are compressed while the occupant is, for all practical purposes, stationary. The acceleration of the man will clearly lag behind that of the seat. At some point therefore, the acceleration of the man must exceed that of the seat to make up for the initial lag. This is acceleration overshoot — the amount by which the acceleration experienced by the occupant exceeds that of the seat — and this factor must always be considered. It is clear therefore that a 'spongy' seat is harmful and will induce acceleration overshoot on ejection.

A good illustration of the effects came during an early ejection when the pilot experienced engine failure at high altitude and had a considerable amount of time to consider and prepare himself for his ejection from the aircraft. He reduced his speed in a shallow glide to 200kt, made sure he was well secured and in the correct position, and fired the seat at 6,000ft. All conditions were favourable yet he experienced a severe pain in his back. Because he landed softly in a tree, there was no landing shock to add to his injury, but he was found to have suffered a fracture of the eighth thoracic vertebra. The fracture occurred because, for personal comfort, he had added a thick foam cushion on top of the already flexible dinghy pack, as a result of which he experienced serious overshoot on ejection. On a test rig accelerometers were mounted on the seat as well as the hips of the occupant who was sitting on a seat pack comprising a parachute, dinghy and water-filled cushion. Not only did the acceleration of the man exceed that of the seat by about 9g, but jolt was also markedly increased when for $^2/_{100}$sec the seat jolt was 220g/sec, while the hip jolt was over 500g/sec. There were therefore two apparently conflicting needs, one to cushion and smooth the effect of acceleration and the other to dampen elasticity of the man/seat system to avoid overshoot. Initially the importance of minimising seat cushions and the importance of strapping in tightly and correctly were constantly stressed: even so, in many early ejections spinal injury was a fairly common occurrence. Poor posture and overshoot could result in any vertebrae being fractured but in about 50% of the cases where this happened fractures occurred in the T11 to L2 area.

In early seats the parachute pack was the standard pilot type held by its own harness to the pilot who sat on it in the aircraft (just as he had done from its introduction as standard life-saving equipment). Later, as seat design changed, the pack moved to his back, and on the very latest seats is in fact contained with the head box. Not only did this progressive repositioning of the 'chute pack help to limit the effect of overshoot, it also enabled the parachute to be where it was needed — above the pilot's head — more quickly, and as aircraft and seat performance increased, savings of fractions of a second were vital.

This has been a somewhat oversimplified account of the early wartime and postwar investigation of the physiological considerations relating to ejection seats, but it is important to set the whole scene in order to indicate that what at first may appear to have been a simple problem to solve required many diverse avenues of research.

The meticulous and painstaking research by James Martin into the spine and how much stress it could take was instrumental in producing the first British ejection seats which satisfied the demanding performance criteria he set. Refinements and changes over the years have of course enormously improved the operating performance, but it has been rare for changes to have been necessary purely for aviation medical reasons. It is fortunate that the country approached James Martin, with his profoundly enquiring mind, to design its first ejection seats, but due recognition must also be given to the German and Swedish scientists who also carried out important research, and solved many associated problems long before James Martin started his research.

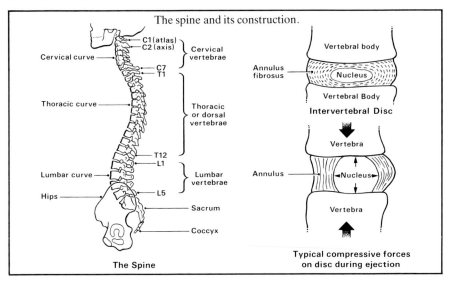

The spine and its construction.

The Spine

Typical compressive forces on disc during ejection

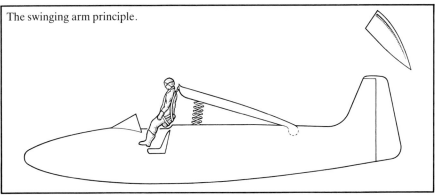

The swinging arm principle.

Above:
Bernard Lynch on the 16ft test rig ready for the first live test shot in 1945.   *Martin-Baker*

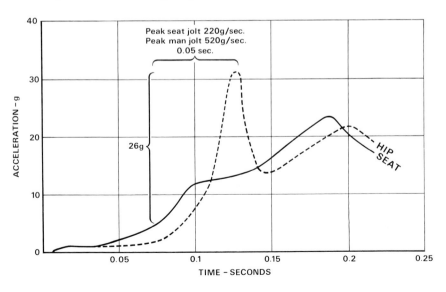

Graph demonstrating overshoot.

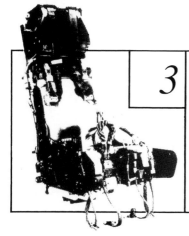

3 | Into The Air

One-hundred-and-eighty tests were performed on the 16ft rig, many being carried out by members of the RAF, RN and MAP. Among the first of the former to try it was Air Cdre E. A. Lumley who at the time was Principal Medical Officer, Fighter Command, and Wg Cdr (later AVM) W. K. Stewart of the Institute of Aviation Medicine. The latter continued to be engaged in the early experimental work, and he contributed immeasurably to the understanding of the physiological aspects of the seat design. But considerable credit must go to Bernard Lynch, who contributed an enormous amount to the design and improvements of early seats and his accumulated operational knowledge of ejection. Endowed with a good physique, cool judgement, coupled with extreme modesty, he was the ideal guinea pig, and his contribution to the success of Martin-Baker seats was quite rightly publicly recognised by the award of the BEM in 1948.

A 65ft rig was built to enable tests which would have been limited by the initial 16ft structure to be carried out. The new rig was used for the first time on 17 August 1945 and the first live shot, with the redoubtable Lynch in occupancy, took place five days later. This was the first use of the double cartridge gun and a height of 26ft 3in was reached, after which Lynch reported that the ride was now very soft with no adverse physiological effects whatsoever. The pressure curve for the 5g case varied little from the 1g case, so the problems relating to acceleration jolt were well on the way to being overcome. It was however also necessary to look at other areas, not the least important of which was operational environment.

In other tests, cartridges were subjected to extremes of temperature, some were cooked for 24hr at 130°F, while others were stored below freezing point so that ice had to be scraped off before they were inserted into the ejection gun. In all cases performance remained unimpaired and the derived pressure curves were not significantly different from those obtained at normal temperatures.

In parallel with the research into physiological aspects, work was also being carried out on the engineering problems of ejection from an actual aircraft, and here the Defiant aircraft mentioned earlier came into its own. The gun turret area was extensively modified to accommodate a seat installation. On 10 May 1945 the aircraft was jacked into an 'in-flight' position, and the seat, loaded with sandbags, was fired into a catch net. This proved the system worked in theory: the next step was to try a shot in the air. This was carried out the following day when the Defiant, with Rotol's Chief Test Pilot Brian Greenstead at the controls, took off

29

from Wittering to carry out what was the first airborne ejection from an aircraft in flight over England. On 17 May 1945 six further tests with dummies in the seat were carried out from the aircraft at varying indicated air speeds (IASs) up to 300mph. The results were encouraging and were looked upon by everyone concerned as a major step forward. The technique used in these tests was to fire the seat with an ejection gun consisting of two telescopic tubes, fired by an explosive cartridge. Once it was clear of the Defiant, a drogue was deployed to stabilise the seat, followed by a 24ft diameter recovery parachute fired by a time delay device. The successful completion and analysis of results saw the introduction of the 65ft rig in August as already described.

It was now necessary to move into the realms of higher speed. Clearly the Defiant had reached its limit, so on 12 September 1945 a contract was placed by the Ministry of Aircraft Production for Martin-Baker to design, develop and manufacture two pilot-type ejection seats and their installation in a high-speed aircraft. A Meteor FIII (EE416) was allocated for this work and delivered to Denham on 6 November 1945, where the ammunition bay behind the cockpit was gutted and modified to accept a seat and its associated equipment. On completion of the installation the Meteor was moved to the company's airfield at Chalgrove in Oxfordshire (still in use for tests today), where on 8 June 1946 a static dummy ejection from the aircraft was made into a net suspended at the top of a 45ft high tower. Just over two weeks later, on 24 June, a dummy ejection was carried out in flight at an IAS of 415mph, using identical techniques to those in the Defiant test programme. This time the delay action equipment on the recovery parachute failed, resulting in the main parachute being deployed too early and bursting, with the resultant loss of the seat. The release mechanism was modified but the same thing happened again. Development of a hydraulic type delay-action release was undertaken, this comprising a hydraulic dashpot interposed between the drogue and the seat. When subjected to the pull of the drogue, the dashpot extended, the speed of this being controlled by the flow of oil from one compartment to another through a calibrated orifice. On completion of the extending period, the pull of the drogue was transferred to the closure pins of the main parachute pack and thence to the canopy of the main parachute which was then deployed.

When this release was first tested, the main parachute did not extract from its container, and examination of a film of the test revealed that the spring-ejector drogue had been drawn into the wake of the seat and became entangled with it. Varying the strength of the ejection springs did not prove satisfactory so a new method had to be sought. James Martin conceived the idea of deploying the drogue by means of an explosive operated gun. This consisted of a barrel containing a piston secured to it by a split pin. The bottom part of the barrel, which housed an explosive cartridge, was screwed into a body containing a spring-loaded firing unit, the sear of which was extracted by a 24ft long static line. The top of the piston was connected by a nylon cord to a safety pin retaining four flaps over the drogue container, and a further extension of the nylon cord connected to the drogue. As the seat ejected, the static line tautened and fired the drogue gun; the energy imparted to the piston sheared the split pin and propelled the piston with considerable force well clear of the seat vortex, taking with it the nylon cord and the drogue which could now deploy properly and stabilise the seat immediately. The idea proved successful, and although subsequently modified in

30

detail, the drogue gun has remained a basic feature of all Martin-Baker seats.

During further test ejections from the Meteor another problem was discovered. It was found that the loads produced at high speed by the drogue were very much higher than anticipated. Using a 3ft diameter drogue with a 9in apex leak hole, 60cwt cables were repeatedly breaking at speeds above 350mph IAS. A great deal of research work and experimentation resulted in a 2ft diameter drogue of special shape manufactured from aircraft linen with a 7½in vent and 12 nylon lines, which functioned perfectly at speeds up to and beyond 500mph.

Time after time tests with the new drogue and its firing gun worked successfully and the day rapidly approached when the dummy would have to be replaced by a live man. James Martin knew that two years' concentrated research was reaching a climax, and only he could give the word that could bring total fulfilment but which at the same time could put a man's life in danger. The final piece in the jigsaw was the confirmation that a human could survive the stress that experiments indicated it could. James Martin has been quoted as saying at the time, 'I hate live tests far worse than the fellows who actually make them, and I hated the very thought of the first one worst of all'.

The day finally chosen was 24 July 1946, the venue Chalgrove airfield near Oxford. Bernard Lynch climbed into the modified former ammunition bay of the Meteor, strapped his considerable bulk to the test ejection seat which was armed just like a primed cannon, and prepared himself for the forthcoming test. The Meteor took-off, climbed to 8,000ft and levelled off. Turning back towards the airfield the pilot increased the speed and as he crossed the boundary the Air Speed Indicator (ASI) nudged 320mph. The moment of truth had come. The dry-mouthed Lynch reached up and with one decisive tug pulled the face blind down.

Those watching on the ground saw a flash of flame and a puff of smoke as the seat left the Meteor and curved high above the cruciform tail. The drogue deployed stabilising the seat, and Lynch sighed with relief: the first part was a success. Sitting in comparative comfort he descended to 7,000ft, but now had to make another major decision: to undo his harness, throw himself into space and pull the ripcord of his personal parachute. He knew this was essential for although he felt secure, he knew that the seat was descending at a speed that would cause certain severe injury if he was still attached to it when it hit the ground. He carried out the necessary actions, kicked the seat away and allowed about 8sec for it to clear him before he pulled his personal parachute ripcord and felt the jolt as it deployed in a white life-saving mushroom above him. After landing and receiving the joyful congratulations of James Martin and his team, Bernard Lynch commented on the moment he actually fired the seat, 'The punch was powerful of course, but not painful, and my first real thrill came when I cleared the cockpit and the slipstream threw me over on my back'.

On this summer day in Oxford, Lynch carved a niche for himself in the annals of aviation history. He went on to make many more test ejections, the next of which was over a year later on 11 August 1947, this time from 6,000ft at an IAS of 200mph. On 29 August 1947 Lynch faced another difficult test shot when he ejected from the Meteor at 12,000ft at an IAS of 420mph (505mph True Air Speed (TAS)). Mentally this must have been as difficult for him as the first ejection since it came just 15 days after another Martin-Baker employee, P. J.

Left:
The 65ft test rig at Denham. *Martin-Baker*

Below left:
An early air test shot of a dummy from the Defiant aircraft. *Martin-Baker*

Above:
Bernard Lynch in the rear cockpit of a modified Meteor III before taking off for the first live ejection on 24 July 1946. *Martin-Baker*

Below:
The modified Meteor III, EE416, used by Martin-Baker for early air tests. *Martin-Baker*

Page, had suffered serious injuries in the first live test at an IAS in excess of 400mph.

Five days after the first successful human airborne ejection in England, Lt Järkenstedt used a Saab seat in deadly earnest, so it is worth taking a brief look at the Swedish seat in comparison with that of Martin-Baker.

As already related, Saab had been experimenting with ejection seats long before Martin-Baker and filed its first patent on 17 October 1941. The seat subsequently installed in the piston-engined J21 and later the jet-powered J21R was one of the first in the world. The seat consisted of a frame and a pan. The frame was based on two tubes, each 1m in length, which were also the guns carrying the firing charges, and served as both the power system and guide rails. They were installed vertically and rested on a spring-loaded adjustment device in the cockpit which enabled the seat to be moved in flight by means of a lever on the left-hand side, into five different positions. The tubes were supported laterally by two pairs of rollers in the aircraft, and a headrest was incorporated into the top ends of them.

It was originally planned to use compressed air from bottles fitted into the airframe in much the same way as Heinkel was experimenting with at the same time, but test shots on a static rig raised considerable doubt as to whether or not sufficient power to clear the pusher propeller of the J21 could be generated. Therefore in co-operation with AB Bofors a powder gas generator was developed using an explosive based on nitroglycerine. This generator was placed centrally on the back of the seat pan and connected by pipes to the ends of the tubes. Firing was accomplished by pulling a handle installed on the right-hand side of the instrument panel. A steel wire passed from this to the seat. When the handle was pulled, valves on the tubes were opened and the generator's explosive charge was activated and directed into the tubes; at the same time a retention mechanism was released, allowing the seat and occupant to be fired from the aircraft.

The seat pan, a very simple dished assembly, was fitted laterally in a slightly eccentric position in relation to the tubular frame. It was fitted with adjustable straps for fastening around the pilot's waist, and the footrests were spring-loaded on the front panel of the seat pan. During the actual ejection the waist straps were automatically detached from the seat as it cleared the airframe. There was also a safety device incorporated into the seat preventing it being fired until the canopy had first been jettisoned. The pilot's parachute was of the personal type placed in the seat pan and carried on a normal harness attached to him in the then traditional way. Early test ejections brought to light several of the problems outlined in relation to Martin-Baker's later experiments. These included the reduction of the powder charge to introduce acceleration in several stages, and the addition of shoulder straps fixed to the back of the seat pan and attached to the waist ones by means of a central locking pin; these straps were also detached automatically during the ejection sequence. It was also decided to replace the firing handle on the instrument panel by one attached to the seat, this becoming a leather strap over the left shoulder. There was no provision for any form of face protection as it was felt that the standard flying helmet and goggles would provide this.

The original design weight of the seat was 20kg, which was reduced to 14kg on the 720 production models manufactured, 358 being installed in J21 aircraft, the rest being used in the B18. For the latter machine the seat pan was mounted symmetrically and the gun tubes reduced by 29mm. In the B18 the same seat was also used for the radio operator and was installed with its back towards the pilot, once again a similar installation to that used by Heinkel for the He219.

Maximum acceleration on production seats was 15g, and the initial velocity was 48.5ft/sec. Initial tests carried out on the static rig used compressed air but as the angle of ejection was gradually increased from 20° to vertical, shortcomings were revealed and the explosive charge method was introduced. In all about 140 ejections were made on the ground followed by three flight tests, one of which was with a scale model. The first full-scale flight test was carried out on 8 January 1942.

Operationally this seat was used on 29 occasions, three of which were from B18 type aircraft. The first use was on 29 July 1946 by Bengt Jarkenstedt, and the last on 19 May 1954. Two of the ejections failed, one at high speed (800km/hr) and one at low level (300m). The lowest altitude and highest speed recorded for successful escapes using the seat was 200m and 500km/hr.

The percentage success rate of the seat was 93%. Comparison of this with later seats can however be misleading, for it must be remembered that with this particular installation, ejection usually occurred at a much lower speed than when the seat became standard equipment on jet aircraft in the early 1950s, and this resulted in more time for the pilot to deploy his personal parachute. It must also be remembered that separation from this early Saab design was also automatic, albeit almost simultaneous with ejection.

So, in June 1947, when the decision to fit Martin-Baker seats to all British military jet aircraft was taken and Bernard Lynch had been the only live ejectee in the UK, a Swedish military pilot and 60 Luftwaffe aircrew had already saved their lives using this method of abandoning their aircraft. The main design parameters of the seat used by Lynch were:

(a) A face screen firing control to ensure correct posture by squaring up the spinal vertebrae and to provide protection to the face from slipstream blast.

(b) A two-cartridge 60ft/sec ejection gun, ensuring an acceptable rate of rise of 'g' forces.

(c) Drogue gun fired by static line after the seat had risen 24ft to ensure the drogue cleared the seat vortex.

(d) Seat stabilised in horizontal position and slowed by the action of a 2ft diameter drogue.

(e) After a delay, controlled by the hydraulic release, the pull of the drogue was transferred from the seat to a 24ft supply drop parachute attached to the seat. This parachute then deployed to support the seat and occupant.

(f) The occupant then unfastened himself from his seat harness, pushed the seat away, and when clear pulled the ripcord of his personal parachute to make a normal descent. The 24ft diameter parachute attached to the seat enabled it to be recovered.

This system worked perfectly and formed the basis on which the first production seats were designed. As work on these progressed, further tests highlighted the need for a variety of modifications, but overall Lynch's history-making ejection created a firm foundation for building and developing the rest of the Martin-Baker range. Following Lynch's first ejection a further series of tests using 200lb of ballast were undertaken and airspeeds progressively increased.

On 14 August a successful test shot at 400mph IAS with 200lb of ballast was accomplished and later the same day it was decided to try the first live ejection at this airspeed. P. J. Page was the man selected but almost from the time he left the Meteor at 6,000ft things started to go wrong. As he left the aircraft and hit the slipstream his feet were torn from the footrests and his legs dangled over the side of the seat. The jolt of the seat recovery parachute opening nearly jerked him from his harness, and he found himself half in and half out of the seat with his body supporting its total weight of some 90lb. He decided to operate the seat release harness and fall free, but in reaching for the release discovered that at sometime in the ejection sequence he had operated the ripcord of his personal parachute which was now wrapped around the seat. He had little choice other than to ride the ejection seat to the ground. The 24ft recovery parachute slowed the descent but even so he hit the runway with a sickening thump and suffered serious injuries including a broken neck. The fact that he was eventually able to give a full account of what had happened led to the development of a system that firmly anchored the occupant to the seat during the initial stages and a cover over the personal parachute ripcord went some way to overcoming the problem of ejectees pulling this in error whilst still fixed to the seat. As previously mentioned, 15 days later Lynch became the first man to eject at over 400mph.

Before moving on to look at the first seats in service it is worth recording that on 28 February 1948 at Chalgrove, Lt Robert Cartier of the French Air Force became the first Frenchman to live-test the Martin-Baker seat. Four months later on 9 June in his native France he also became the fastest ejectee to date when he carried out a test at Bretigny at an IAS of 515mph. On 11 September the same year Bernard Lynch carried out the first ejection over Northern Ireland at Belfast, and seven days later at Chalgrove, Sqn Ldr J. S. Fifield — a name that was to become famous in later experimental ejections — made the first of his many in-flight test ejections, which he recalls as follows:

'The seat used on this occasion was the same as the production seat except that it was fitted with a 28ft canopy for preservation purposes. Normal flying kit was worn but as there was no radio intercommunication in the Meteor, a normal Gosport helmet was used. On the run in we found that cloud base was 3,000ft but rather than abandon the flight, the pilot climbed to the prearranged height (4,000ft) where, after levelling off, he passed the "get ready" signal. The face blind can easily be reached and pulled out some of the way. On receiving the "GO" signal I pulled the blind the full distance which fired the seat cartridge. I felt what seemed to be a half-compression explosion which shot the seat out of the aircraft with surprisingly little "g" effect. The blind is designed with a close fit and because of this I felt no blast whatsoever on my face. The drogue gun was fired when the static line was fully extended but I could not hear the detonations. The resulting tug indicated that the drogue had functioned correctly. After a brief pause in the retarding phase, I would normally have released my harness, fallen out of the seat and carried out a normal parachute descent, but, as already mentioned, this particular seat was fitted with a 28ft canopy which duly opened after an hydraulic timing device had ensured adequate retardation.

'The subsequent jerk was not uncomfortable and it felt considerably less than that usually experienced in a conventional parachute jump. After enjoying a few pleasant moments in the seat, I released the Sutton harness and at 3,000ft used my ordinary parachute.

'Although the ejection drill is simple enough, I consider it essential that the subject, before using the ejection seat, should receive instruction on the training rig to familiarise himself with the correct sequence and method of operation. This training will undoubtedly become a part of the normal service emergency drill. I have confidence in this invention and would, without hesitation, gladly repeat the performance.'

The Squadron Leader's comments about familiarisation on a test rig for service pilots was of course sound commonsense. In February 1946, Martin-Baker had received a contract from the Ministry of Aircraft Production to design, supply and erect a 50ft training rig for instructing pilots in the use of ejection seat and the standardisation of escape drill. At this time the process of ejection was:

(A) Jettison the hood.
(B) Withdraw feet into the ejection position on the footrests and at the same time grasp the handle of the face blind.
(C) Pull the face blind firmly out and downwards whereupon ejection occurs immediately.

The training rig allowed the whole procedure to be carried out and fired the seat up the inclined guide rails. It incorporated a mock-up cockpit complete with a jettisonable hood which had a safety device that prevented the pilot operating the ejection gun before jettisoning the hood.

The rig was erected on 8 February 1948 at RAF Chivenor and Martin-Baker staff immediately started to instruct service personnel in its operation. Thus whilst work was progressing on the design and production of the first line of seats for use in aircraft such as the Meteor, Attacker, Wyvern, Canberra, Venom and Sea Hawk, the men who would use them operationally were adding a new dimension to their escape drills.

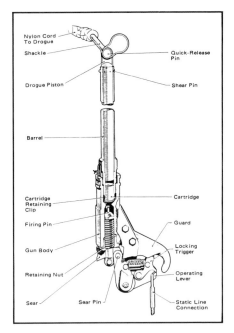

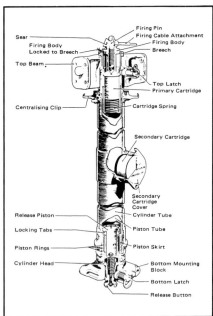

Early design of drogue gun, fired by 24ft
static line.

Sixty foot per second ejection gun.

Below:
Sqn Ldr John Fifield making the first live test ejection from a modified Meteor T7 (WA634)
at Chalgrove. *Martin-Baker*

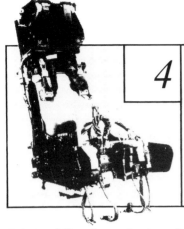

4 Into Production And Service

Prior to full-scale production of the Mk 1, an order was placed by Saunders-Roe for an intermediate design for use in its Saro A1 jet-powered flying boat fighter. This has become known as the Pre-Mk 1 and lacked many refinements of the seat that was to enter full-scale production. The Mk 1 seat, which was used successfully on over 50 occasions, was constructed of light alloy, and together with its guide rails (also fabricated from the same material), drogue, pilot's parachute, dinghy pack, emergency oxygen and water bottle, weighed 172lb of which 143lb was ejected weight. Among the features, some of which are still identifiable in the latest seats, were:

(i)   The two-cartridge ejection gun.

(ii) The automatic gas pressure-operated release mechanism incorporated in the ejection gun which unlocks the ejection gun piston from the cylinder immediately the first cartridge is fired.

(iii) The adjustable seat pan which gave the advantage of raising and lowering it only instead of the whole seat, and enabled a lower cockpit canopy line to be adopted.

(iv) Floating footrests hinged to the seat pan frame and spring loaded downwards so that they remained at floor level independent of the seat pan adjustment. The feet could therefore be slid back from the rudder pedals without raising them from the floor, which could be difficult, if not impossible, with the aircraft subjected to vertical acceleration at the time of escape.

(v)   The face blind method of firing the first cartridge giving the dual advantage of supporting the pilot's head and protecting his face.

(vi) The drogue gun method of withdrawing and developing the stabilising drogue.

(vii) The retractable type seat pan raising handle which allowed the cockpit to be kept down to the minimum width, as it no longer protruded beyond the seat pan thigh guards, the width of which was determined by the basic physical size of the pilot.

(viii) The Martin-Baker back-type dinghy pack which incorporated a rigid tubular framework which maintained the pack's dimensions. This also contained the cradle stowage for the emergency oxygen bottle which was designed to be readily accessible for examination and replenishment.

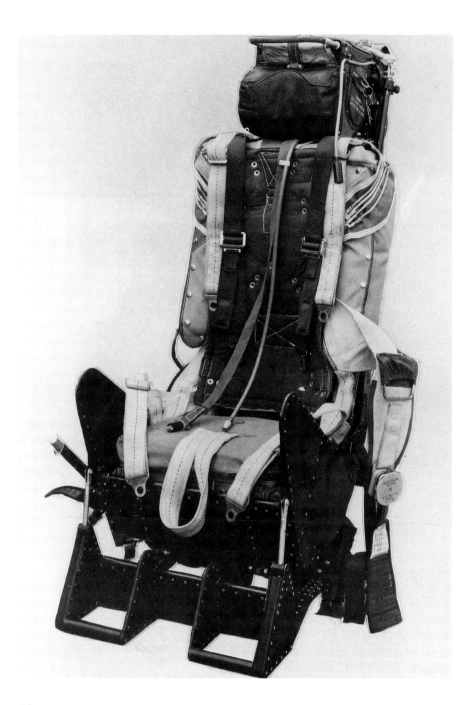

Above:
Martin-Baker Mk 1 ejection seat. *Martin-Baker*

40

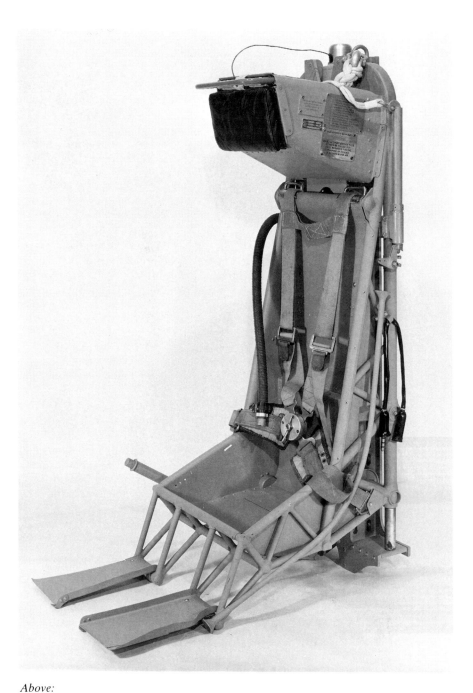

Above:
This is a pre-production Mk 1 seat as fitted to the Saunders-Roe SRA1 flying boat fighter.
The same seat without the footrests was fitted to the AW52 Flying Wing. *Martin-Baker*

(ix) Seat thigh guards integral with the seat pan to prevent the occupant's legs being blown apart by the slipstream or thrown outwards by centrifugal force should the seat spin on the drogue after ejection.

This seat was standard equipment by 1950 on RAF and Royal Navy jet fighters entering service, and similar to that used in the first emergency escape which occurred on 30 May 1949 when test pilot John Lancaster ejected from his AW52 (see Chapter 12).

Introduction into service aircraft was not without its difficulties. Almost without exception, manufacturers claimed that the seat could not be fitted to their aircraft without major structural alterations to cockpit areas.

Air and Naval staffs were at first reluctant to give the seats support in the face of so much opposition, which exaggerated the costs and disruption to aircraft availability schedules that such a major modification involved. There were also pilots who said that they were very reluctant to fly with explosive cartridges attached to their seats. In spite of all this, James Martin's determination and leadership won the day and in a relatively short space of time the now familiar red warning triangle, indicating that an ejection seat was fitted, began to appear just below the cockpit rim of all new jet fighters and bombers. Lt P. L. McDermot of the Royal Navy Air Fighting Development Unit based at RAF West Raynham was the first service pilot to save his life using a Martin-Baker Mk 1 seat when his Attacker had engine failure at 7,500ft on 20 March 1951. Sgts Tollett and Tickner of the RAF followed in July 1951 and in August WO R. Gutherie of No 77 Squadron RAAF became the first jet pilot to save his life with an ejection seat following air-to-air combat in Korea. (The full story of Gutherie's ejection is featured in the second part of this book.)

On 15 September 1951 the new escape system had an unscheduled but spectacular public demonstration when Flg Off L. J. Smith of No 63 Squadron, flying a Meteor F8 in a Battle of Britain display at Waterbeach, collided with another Meteor and lost his tail unit. Smith's aircraft went into a flat spin which made it difficult for him to reach the face blind. He succeeded in so doing only at 1,500ft and subsequently made a perfect ejection. In writing to Martin-Baker after the event he said, 'My sole criticism of your ejection seat is that the operating handle does not quite fall "readily to hand" '.

He was flying with the seat pan in the fully lowered position and had to look for the handle before pulling it, as his hands were being pushed sideways by the forces acting on the aircraft. Flg Off Smith suggested that it would be far easier to reach the handle if it projected about 2in further forward. He claimed that this might make all the difference when full upward arm movement was restricted by a tight safety harness. This is the earliest example of an ejectee's comment being adopted by the Denham design team and, together with others, it was incorporated into later seats.

However, it was not all success and glory. On 21 December 1951 a USAF pilot and navigator ejected at 8,000ft from a Canberra in the USA. The pilot ejected through the canopy and the navigator through the frangible hatch. Both ejections were successful but the navigator subsequently drowned when he landed in a river. Less than a month later Wg Cdr Foster was killed on 12 January 1952 when he ejected from a prototype Vickers Valiant near Bournemouth. The pilot, Jock

Bryce of Vickers, ejected successfully when the aircraft caught fire and suffered structural failure but Wg Cdr Foster struck the tail fin; his seat was not fitted with the telescopic gun which was later fitted to ejection seats. The first RAF fatality occurred on 20 January 1952 when Sgt Richmond flying Meteor F8 WE868 and Flg Off G. M. Smith in WE864 collided over Church Fenton. Both men ejected but Sgt Richmond delayed his release from his seat and suffered injuries from which he died. Flg Off Smith found himself inverted at 9,000ft in a diving turn, and like his namesake had initial difficulty in reaching the face blind. He eventually achieved this but received crushed dorsal vertebrae in the ejection.

About 50 successful ejections were made using the earliest type of Martin-Baker seat, and there can be no doubt that these justified its introduction into service. But it also highlighted the need to cater for cases where injury, unconsciousness brought on by ejection at high altitude, disorientation and lack of time at low level had to be looked at. In 1952 and 1953 about 30% of the 32 ejections by RAF airmen proved to be fatal. The reason for this was that the seat was basically a simple device which did nothing more than get the occupant away from his aircraft, then left him to his own devices. The stress of the actual ejection — and in some cases the short time available — prevented some escapees from actually taking any action to free themselves from the seat. Others hesitated too long, fumbled, or got the sequence of events out of order. To understand the situation it is helpful to appreciate that when an ejection took place at, say, 1,000ft, the seat and occupant would hit the ground in 5sec if no action to deploy the parachute was taken. So it is easy to see that from such a height a man would have just 5sec in which to carry out two or three sequential actions in order to survive. Studying tests and fatal ejections, James Martin saw the need to provide a mechanism to remove these actions and to make the whole ejection sequence from the time of initiation until the man was under a developed parachute, totally automatic.

The solution turned out to be simple but also created another problem. In the Mk 2 automatic seat, the position of the parachute and dinghy pack were reversed: it was the former moving upwards to the pilot's back, and the latter to the seat pan, that made it easier for the stabilising drogue to now be used to deploy the parachute. To do this the drogue would need to separate from the seat and transfer its pull to the pilot's parachute at exactly the right moment. At the same time a method of unfastening the seat straps and releasing the occupant (together with his dinghy and survival equipment) also had to be perfected. On the Mk 1 seat the drogue was attached by a solid shackle; on the Mk 2 this was replaced by a 'scissor' shackle which opened automatically at a predetermined time. A clockwork Time Release Unit (TRU) was devised and bolted to the top of one of the side beams of the seat. As the seat rose on ejection, a static line tripped the unit which then ran for 5sec before releasing a plunger in the mechanism which opened the scissor shackle releasing the drogue from the seat. At the same time the mechanism unlocked the seat harness by pulling on a cable which rotated the face plate of the modified harness release box. As the drogue pulled away from the seat, its pull was transferred to a canvas apron, positioned between the parachute and its container, which tautened and tipped the occupant forward out of the seat. Attached to this apron was a withdrawal line which released the parachute pack security pins and withdrew the parachute. At the same time as the drogue pulled free of the scissor shackle, the face blind was also released thus freeing the occupant of all attachments to the seat, and leaving him to descend in the normal way. To overcome the problem of the automatic sequence operating at high altitude where lack of oxygen and frostbite could prove fatal, a barostat was fitted to the TRU to stop it operating above 10,000ft. This comprised an aneroid capsule which engaged in the timer's operating wheel, locking it until the release height was reached: the seat and occupant therefore descended through the cold and rarified air stabilised by the drogue and provided with oxygen turned on automatically during ejection. In any design care must be taken to overcome the possibility of failure of any component, and in order to guard against such an event occurring with the TRU, provision was made for manual separation to be carried out. This necessitated some means of being able to disconnect the parachute withdrawal line, which was now connected to the drogue via the apron, before the occupant unfastened his safety harness. The answer was the provision of a slide disconnect pin in the line, located within the parachute pack and operated by an additional 'D' ring on the parachute harness. In the event of failure of the TRU after ejection the drill was to first pull the 'D' ring, unfasten the seat harness, push clear of the seat, and when clear pull the personal parachute ripcord. The two 'D' rings were positioned close to each other, but the one which activated the occupant's parachute was covered by a canvas flap which was removed on operation of the first one, thus preventing an incorrect sequence being initiated. The final modification was to improve the drogue gun which on the Mk 1 seat had been fired by a 24ft static line. The new one was operated by a 1sec timer and tripped by a short static line attached to the aircraft.

By August 1953 a retrospective modification programme in which Mk 1 seats were modified to Mk 2 standard was well under way. Those in use by the RAF were modified at the Martin-Baker factory and those by the Royal Navy on site by Navy parties who had been trained for the task.

Just as it was a Royal Navy pilot who was the first British military user of the Mk 1 seat, it now also fell to the Senior Service to record the first use in 'anger' of a Mk 2 automatic seat: this time the pilot was Lt C. R. Bushe, who on 15 July 1953 used a Mk 2A seat from his Attacker (see 'Double Trouble').

The automatic seat was a major landmark in reducing fatalities which in the 33 ejections recorded by RAF crews in 1954 occurred only three times. It was not only in emergency situations where the new automatic and barostatic controlled seats came into their own, but also on the very rare occasions when accidental ejection occurred. One of the earliest of these happened in April 1956 when Flt Lt R. Watson of the Central Fighter Establishment (CFE) at West Raynham was fired from his Hunter at 42,000ft! Flt Lt Watson was carrying out practice interceptions with a Canberra and had no intention whatsoever of parting company with his aircraft. But unknown to him the top latch of his Mk 2H seat had not been properly secured in the aircraft during a routine service. As he dived on the Canberra at an IAS of 250kt, the seat moved in its guide rails and the prime charge was fired. Later Flt Lt Watson reported that he was ejected through the canopy, and had heard the drogue gun fire whilst he was still in the aircraft. Not having operated his seat, his face blind was still in its stowage, and his inner and outer helmet were torn away as he hit the slipstream. During the free fall of some

32,000ft he remained conscious although during the initial acceleration period he did grey out. The seat remained stable throughout and on reaching 10,000ft the automatic sequence worked perfectly. His parachute descent was quite normal although mainly due to his inexperience and a 20kt surface wind he broke an ankle on landing.

Flt Lt Watson's ejection was the highest on record at that time but in April 1958 two RAF officers also used an early mark of seat to escape from an experimental Canberra aircraft at 56,000ft. Flt Lt de Salis and Flg Off P. Lowe were testing a Mk 6 Canberra fitted with a Napier Twin Scorpion rocket motor mounted in the rear of the bomb-bay. The objective was to practice firing the rocket at high level, and on reaching the selected height de Salis levelled the aircraft, selected his switches, then asked Lowe in the navigator's seat to activate his. The rocket fired and its thrust took over from the residual power of the Avons to climb steadily to just above 56,000ft. On completion of the burn a slow descent was started but there was still some High Test Peroxide (HTP) left in the tank so it was decided to make another burn to use most of it before jettisoning the rest and returning to base. This time as the motor was fired the aircraft pitched violently, the nose and starboard wing dropped, and an explosive decompression followed. The cockpit filled with white smoke and dust swirled around, at which point Flg Off Lowe decided it was high time he wasn't around. His own words describe what happened:

'I went rapidly through the ejection procedure — I am bound to say without reference to the pilot — jettisoned the hatch and pulled the blind over my helmet. I do not remember the actual ejection, but clearly the seat worked, the drogue gun fired and the drogue stabilised the seat. I remember falling away from the seat feeling fairly uncomfortable due to my pressure suit, anti "g" trousers and helmet being fully pressurised; breathing was extremely difficult.

'As I fell the pressure increased and I became more comfortable. My hands were very cold (indeed the only damage I suffered was frostbite on my fingers, fortunately with no permanent damage). Otherwise I was OK and really surprisingly unworried, presumably because I thought that the hard bit was over. The barostat worked perfectly and I am ashamed to say that I didn't even look up to see if the parachute had fully deployed. Soon after, I landed in a field of stubble, rolled on my back and just waited for help to arrive. I was deaf due to the decompression, lisping due to having bitten my tongue on landing, and I couldn't undo the zip at the back of my pressure helmet due to my frostbitten fingers. I was quite relieved when an ATC cadet with his father arrived, unbuckled me and took me to Bakewell Cottage Hospital. Both Pete de Salis and myself were convinced that the other could not have survived. The fact that we both did, and with no permanent injury, still amazes me.'

These two examples from very high altitudes would not have been possible without automatic seats, but what about the situation at the other end of the scale, that is, very low level including ejection from the runway? Such a situation had already been foremost in the minds of the designers and at the time of both described escapes a test ejection from ground level had already been made. The Mk 2 automatic seats were successful in providing escape from the aircraft then in service, but there was still room for improvement especially at high speeds and low levels. Additionally aircraft such as the V-bombers and Javelin with their high tails made it necessary to look at increasing the ejection trajectory.

To do this without increasing peak acceleration, peak 'g' and jolt, beyond the limits of human tolerance, an ejection gun with a stroke of 72in was designed to replace the existing 60ft/sec gun, and this provided a velocity of 80ft/sec. The gun consisted of three tubes, two of which telescoped inside the main outer one, powered by one primary and four auxiliary charges. The latter were arranged in two pairs and when the primary charge was fired, the innermost tube was unlocked by the generated pressure and began to rise, together with the intermediate tube, carrying the seat and occupant with it. After extending 16in, the lower two auxiliary cartridge ports were uncovered allowing the flame to ignite the first pair of cartridges, and a further 9½in extension uncovered and fired the second pair of auxiliary cartridges. The gun continued to extend until the intermediate tube was arrested by a flange on the outer tube, the shock being cushioned by 15 hollow gas-filled rings. The innermost tube continued extending until it broke away from the gun, carrying the seat and occupant clear of the aircraft. The introduction of the 80ft/sec gun resulted in a gain of trajectory height at low altitude, and to enable full advantage of this to be taken and therefore increase the chances of safe escape from the ground, thought was turned to speeding up separation. As mentioned earlier the TRU introduced a 5sec delay before releasing the drogue scissor shackle: whilst this was short it was still too long at low level. The 24ft drogue in use on Mk 1 and early Mk 2 automatic seats took 5sec to stream the main parachute, so it was obvious that a drogue of constant diameter would only achieve efficiency at a certain combination of height and speed.

The time interval chosen had been selected to allow the speed to drop from the highest probable ejection speed to one for safe deployment of the main parachute, in other conditions its performance was less than efficient. Intensive development led to the introduction of the duplex drogue system for the Mk 3 seat. This comprised two drogues in tandem, one of 22in diameter called the controller, and a larger main one of 5ft diameter. On ejection, the controller drogue was automatically extracted by the drogue gun, and when deployed brought the seat into a horizontal attitude, then towed the main drogue from its container. The main drogue then performed as before by streaming the parachute on separation and lifting the occupant clear of the seat. The controller did in fact carry out two very important functions: firstly it put the seat into a horizontal attitude so that deceleration on the seat and occupants were linear, and consequently more tolerable, and second it prevented explosive opening of the main drogue. In tests when the 5ft drogue was deployed without the controller at 600mph and a height of 150ft, it was torn to shreds, the drogue producing such violent loads that the face screen was torn and the seat harness broken. With the controller employed under similar conditions, none of the components showed any signs of distress. Similarly, the main drogue prevented the explosive opening of the parachute, thus opening shocks were reduced to within the strength limitations of the parachute and physical limitations of the body.

Examination of reports from ejections indicated that in some cases injury had occurred because the ejectees' legs flailed about during ejection. It was therefore decided to further improve the new seat by adding some form of leg restraint system.

Several options were considered including one in which guards folded over the legs. Finally it was decided to use a method of securing the legs to the seat by nylon cords. The arrangement consisted of two reinforced nylon cords each connected to the cockpit floor by a shear pin designed to pull free at the load needed to ensure the legs were held back against the forward edge of the seat pan. The other end of each cord was passed through snubbing units fixed to the forward face of the seat pan, then through metal rings on webbing garters strapped to the occupant's legs. The two free ends of the cords were then connected to the harness release box. The cords allowed free movement of the legs whilst seated in the cockpit, but on ejection, tightened up between the snubbing units and the harness release box before breaking away from the floor, thereby securing them to the seat where they were firmly held until the harness was released during the separation action.

Incorporation of the duplex drogue enabled the time delay between ejection and the streaming of the main parachute to be reduced from 5sec to 3sec. At the same time the delay in the firing of the drogue gun was reduced from 1sec to ½sec. These modifications, as well as the addition of leg restraints and the 80ft/sec gun, took the Mk 3 seat one massive jump ahead of its predecessors, allowing safe ejection from 50ft above ground level at 130kt.

To achieve ground level ejection capability the next step was to reduce still further the delay between ejection and the streaming of the parachute, from 3sec to 1½sec. James Martin considered this possible and tests with the 80ft/sec gun and time release mechanism set to 1½sec confirmed that ground level ejection was possible with the aircraft level and at a speed not less than 90kt. To prove this he decided that a live ground level demonstration should be carried out. When his intention became known, it was violently opposed and he received a telegram from the Ministry of Supply forbidding the use of the Meteor that was on loan from them, on the grounds that the risks were too great. When protests were made, two directors from the Ministry's Research & Development Department went to Denham to show James Martin the folly of his ways.

With his Irish charm and sheer technical brilliance he soon persuaded the men from the Ministry that the danger was not as great as they imagined. So, in spite of the original opposition, on 3 September 1955 the redoubtable John Fifield fired himself from the modified rear cockpit of Meteor 7 WA634 during its take-off run at Chalgrove. This particular aircraft had been allocated to Martin-Baker in January 1952 and, in addition to the necessary modifications to the rear seat compartment, it was also fitted with the E1/44 high-speed rear fuselage and tail unit. This Meteor served Martin-Baker until April 1962 by which time it had been involved in 670 test ejections including more than 50 with the rocket-assisted seat. On the Mk 3 seat used by Fifield the delay was set at 1½sec and the aircraft had reached 90kt when he fired the seat. Just 6sec after pulling the face blind he was safely back on the ground proving to all the sceptics that survivable ground level ejection was possible.

It is interesting to note that on this occasion Fifield used a standard 24ft Irvin air parachute, although initially he had expressed a preference for a 28ft parachute. However, dummy runs revealed that the smaller canopy deployed quicker, opening some 35ft higher than the larger one. Following this impressive demonstration James Martin next day received a telegram from the Air Minister congratulating him and all concerned on their achievement.

On 25 October 1955 the remarkable John Fifield, who seemed to have an insatiable appetite for adventure, tested the same Mk 3 seat at the other end of the height scale when he ejected from the same aircraft at 40,000ft. For the first 15sec of the free fall to 10,000ft the seat was fully stabilised, but after that it settled into a slow spin rotating between 15 and 20rpm about the longitudinal axis before disappearing into a patch of stratus cloud. When seen again Fifield was suspended from his parachute and landed lafely. He reported that he had not felt any unpleasant sensation from the spinning and that the seat had been remarkably stable throughout the free fall. This and subsequent tests proved that the Mk 3 seat was quite capable of being used with total safety from high altitude with protection of the occupant being provided by the seat structure, face blind, leg restraint, while the firing handle gave a positive hand-hold which prevented flailing of the arms. The face screen also helped to hold the oxygen mask in position, enabling the occupant to breath from his emergency supply which was turned on as the seat fired.

Aside from the seat, another important aspect that had been costing time when every second counted was the jettisoning of the aircraft's cockpit canopy. Service experience indicated that vital time was being used to operate jettison equipment as well as carrying out pre-ejection drill. Battle damage or certain aerodynamic conditions might well prevent the canopy departing the airframe even though the correct jettison procedures had been followed. In such cases it was quite possible that firing of the seat would result in it colliding with the unlocked canopy and becoming entangled with it. Another aspect that had come to light in many reports was that even when the canopy was jettisoned and departed smoothly, the resultant entry of slipstream into the cockpit could make it hard for the pilot to reach the face blind. The answer was to provide an explosive jettisoning system powerful enough to force the canopy clear under all conditions, and to link this to the operation of the ejection seat firing handle.

The system developed by Martin-Baker consisted of a unit bolted to the rear of the ejection seat guide rail, containing a canopy jettison breech, together with a 1sec delay mechanism. On operating the firing handle the sear of the canopy jettison gun was withdrawn, the cartridge detonated, and gases passed through piping to two canopy jettison jacks. The expanding gases forced the pistons of the jacks upwards, first operating the canopy locks then raising it for the slipstream to carry it away from the aircraft. At the same time as the canopy jettison cartridge fired, a time delay mechanism was tripped. This ran for 1sec at the end of which the main ejection gun fired, thus allowing the canopy to be well clear of the aircraft before ejection occurred. This simple but effective device ensured that once the pilot had started the ejection sequence he would be carried clear of the aircraft and no time would be wasted in carrying out pre-ejection actions, which could well prejudice his chances of survival. Before the introduction of the automatic canopy jettison system some pilots had experienced difficulties as foreseen by James Martin.

On 6 June 1952, Flg Off Davies of No 54 Squadron suffered serious fractures of his right leg when he ejected from his Meteor Mk 8 and the seat collided with the canopy; on 30 November 1953, Plt Off Elford-Eggleton made the first recorded ejection through the aircraft's canopy when his Meteor suffered a structural failure at 8,000ft, and on 24 July 1954, Flg Off Bennet, again in a Mk 8 Meteor, went through his canopy on a 2E automatic seat at less than 1,000ft with the aircraft inverted. He was particularly lucky as at the time he was not wearing a 'bone dome', and surprisingly enough was not rendered unconscious, his only injuries being slight bruises to the head and body, the latter received on landing. In reporting this last ejection Flg Off Bennet's CO, Gp Capt P. G. St. G. O'Brian, in a letter to James Martin, said '. . . I read with the greatest of interest your scheme whereby the hood is shot off a fraction of a second before the seat is shot out.' The explosive bolt canopy jettison system on the Canberra had caused problems during emergencies and on several occasions there were reports of the canopy failing to leave the aircraft and blowing back into the pilot's face, causing injury and in some cases death. An instruction was therefore given to Canberra pilots to jettison through the hood, and the first man to do this was Flg Off C. B. Crombie from a B Mk 2 aircraft fitted with a Mk 1C manual seat on 20 December 1954. Crombie's aircraft became uncontrollable during a spin, and at 10,000ft with an airspeed of over 500kt he ejected, suffering only superficial injuries. Unfortunately the two navigators did not eject and were killed.

On 13 March 1955, Sub-Lt Michael Cahill ejected from his Sea Hawk FGA4 using a Mk 2D automatic seat at 500ft and an IAS of 450kt with the aircraft banked at 50° and rolling very rapidly. His experience was typical of that which must have resulted in the deaths of some pilots, for he did not hesitate or go through preliminary ejection drills which included manual jettisoning of the canopy. As soon as the aircraft started its uncontrollable roll, he pulled the firing handle and went through the canopy feeling a hefty bang as his helmet hit it. His feet were still on the rudder bar and he grazed his ankle on the high pressure fuel cock as he left the aircraft, his only other injuries being a cut eyebrow from the broken Perspex and a stiff back from the actual ejection. The Sub-Lt estimated that he was under his fully deployed parachute for only 4sec before hitting the water, and was rescued 20min later by a Whirlwind helicopter from his carrier, HMS *Centaur*.

These random examples not only indicate that survival with both early manual and automatic seats was possible from all heights and attitudes, but how a few seconds saved in not carrying out what were then vital actions, possibly made the difference between life and death. The lessons learned in operation and the feedback to Martin-Baker was, and continues to be, vital and instrumental in seat development.

The first recorded successful ejection using a Mk 3 seat fitted with automatic canopy ejection equipment was on 8 December 1955 when Sqn Ldr A. D. Dick ejected from a spinning Javelin, one of the aircraft that had been in James Martin's mind when he designed the high trajectory 80ft/sec ejection gun; this was also the first ejection from a Javelin aircraft.

Before bringing to an end this look at the early development and production of Martin-Baker seats which set the standards for subsequent designs, it is worth recording the story of the first use of a Mk 3 seat from a Vampire T11 trainer. On 2 November 1955, Master Pilot Evans and his pupil, Plt Off Robert Jago of No 101 course at 8 FTS Swinderby, were carrying out aerobatics at 15,000ft. The

Vampire got into an inverted spin during recovery from a stall turn and at 12,000ft the instructor gave the order to eject and manually jettisoned the canopy. A few seconds later he heard Plt Off Jago's seat fire and watched the student leave the aircraft — in fact, in the close confines of the Vampire's cockpit he actually brushed Evans's shoulder as he left. Master Pilot Evans then reached up for his handle but due to a combination of negative 'g' and the roaring slipstream, his hands were blown upwards and the seat failed to fire. He managed to keep his grasp on the screen and eventually pulled it down to his chest which successfully activated the seat. After leaving the aircraft the seat failed to stabilise and he sensed that he was falling very fast. A glance behind confirmed that the drogue was not correctly deployed and he attempted to untangle it. This proved unsuccessful and as he knew that he was now below 10,000ft and nothing had happened he decided to use the manual override 'D' ring. He recalled that he did not remember unfastening his harness and suspected that the barostatic control had done this. After a short struggle he managed to leave the seat and operate the ripcord of his parachute which deployed very quickly. Soon afterwards he saw both ejection seats and the aircraft's canopy go past him. Master Pilot Evans suffered severe lacerations to both feet which he believes happened when they hit the lower edge of the instrument panel, because as he readily admits, he did not tighten his leg-restraining cords sufficiently. He also felt that if he had been wearing flying boots instead of shoes he might well not have received the cuts. His bone-dome and all other equipment stayed firmly in place. Meanwhile Plt Off Jago experienced a perfect ejection and two days later he wrote to Martin-Baker thanking them for the efficient working of the seat. He concluded his letter with the comment, 'it increases a pupil's confidence enormously to know that the seat will extract him from his mistakes'. This simple statement could have been echoed not only by pupil pilots but all aircrew who by this time were regarding the ejection seat as a vital necessity and not something to be eyed with suspicion.

Left:
Sqn Ldr John Fifield, who did much of the pioneer testing work, especially on ground-level ejection seats. *Martin-Baker*

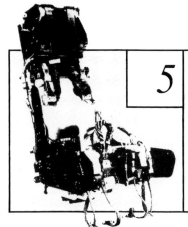

5 | The Swedish Scene

As briefly mentioned in an earlier chapter, Saab-Scania was a pioneer in the field of escape systems and its contribution to the development of the ejection seat is often overlooked. Design and development started in 1940 when the country was virtually cut off from the rest of the world. Early development led to the production of the seat used in J21 aircraft, and to date all Saab military aircraft since the J21 have been fitted with the company's own design of ejection seat. The philosophy behind the design, from the earliest days to the latest rocket seats, has been greatly influenced by the Air Force's points of view and close co-operation with the Defence Material Administration. One of the most important features retained with all the aircraft types has been the parachute pack as a separate unit divorced from the rest of the seat both as regards hardware and function. In the latest seats, however, the restraining and parachute harnesses have been integrated, both components being coupled together by a parachute arming device active upon separation. Another important feature followed by the Saab team has been the separation of the occupant from the seat as soon as possible after ejection. A great deal of effort has been made in relation to the rocket seat and its drogue chute, in order to stabilise and retard the seat after high-speed ejections. The reason for this is the need to take into account the occupant's best acceleration tolerance, this being facing forward with his spine perpendicular to the slipstream.

Within the factory grounds at Linköping there is a testing area, surrounded by a protective rampart, for weapons tests, seat track ejections and static tests on explosives. Tests using the Dodge truck (previously described) are carried out on the company's airfield, whilst flight tests usually take place over one of the paratroop school's training fields at Forsvik, north of Karlsborg. High altitude testing is carried out at the RFN base in Västerbotten.

Within the grounds of the Saab factory a 13m rig with an inclination of 60° was built and later replaced by a 30m track which is still in use. From the earliest tests the Swedish engineers used dummies in various sizes. Each of these was built using a skeleton framework with simulated joints, muscles and tissues and weight distribution as close to the human form as possible. Later all joints and relevant parts were telemetered for analysis. In the flight test programme, Saab used several different aircraft starting with the B3 (Ju86) and Saab B17. The high performance J32 Lansen proved to be a highly satisfactory test platform and one was modified in much the same way as the Meteor T7 was in England. Most flight tests were carried out from Lansen 32 502, which was also supported by an SK35C Draken.

The original Type 21 seat aroused a great deal of international interest and teams from France and the USA visited Sweden to see it and possibly negotiate manufacturing rights, but none of the talks resulted in concrete proposals although a test seat was sent to America. The Type 29 seat was however sold under licence to Folland Aircraft Ltd in England and after several modifications was installed in the company's Gnat trainer and lightweight fighter. Other British manufacturers also showed some interest, but nothing came of this and Martin-Baker seats became standard in the British aircraft industry.

Some Saab seats were exported with J29 aircraft to Austria, which also used the equipment in the SB105 trainers purchased from Sweden. The J35 Drakens with rocket seats were sold to Denmark and Finland but the seats were never exported as separate items. Neither the Lansen nor its seat was subject to any export sales.

The basic design of the J21 seat and its subsequent use in service including the first successful ejection by a Swedish Air Force pilot, has already been dealt with. Space prevents a detailed analysis of all the work carried out by the company, but the lineage of the seats and their development is outlined to give the reader a basic knowledge of the path followed by Saab.

The J29, known worldwide as the 'Flying Barrel', was a single-seat fighter powered by a DH Ghost engine, and made its maiden flight on 1 September 1948. The seat installed was similar in overall design to the original Type 21 and fitted in the aircraft with a backward tilt of 30°, which not only reduced frontal area but also increased the pilot's resistance to acceleration during recovery from high-speed dives. The aircraft's one-piece canopy was jettisoned by a cartridge and compressed air which was activitated by the initial firing sequence of the ejection seat. The tubular frame seat pan and headrest of the earlier design were retained as were the roller supports and seat adjustment. The charge was a three-stage one using 60 grams of explosive placed centrally in the upper part of the frame and connected by pipes to the upper ends of the tubes.

It was originally planned to operate the seat by two firing straps located by the pilot's shoulders, these ensuring that on ejection both arms were held fast. However, the straps were replaced by a face blind (referred to by the Swedish designers as a 'curtain'), located in the headrest in the same way as that preferred from the very beginning on Martin-Baker seats. The seat was also fitted with a reserve firing lever located in the centre under the seat pan, where it could be reached more easily if unfavourable 'g' forces prevented the occupant reaching up for the overhead firing screen. The full harness had adjustable straps and a central locking system, the shoulder straps being attached to a yoke from which a line went to a lockable spring-loaded duct. This was all part of a planned automatic harness release device operated by a static line attached to the aircraft, but this was however omitted from the first series which had completely manual harness release systems. A further innovation of the Type 29 seat was the provision of spring-loaded foot supports which were intended to prevent flailing as well as to protect the legs. The parachute was a back type carried by the occupant and not attached as an integral part of the seat. It was opened manually and contained an emergency oxygen cylinder. The emergency equipment was housed in a soft pack in the seat pan and attached to the parachute harness.

During service many of the developments incorporated in the Type 32 seat designed for the Lansen were retrospectively fitted to the Type 29, these including a mechanically operated harness release mechanism housed in the rear of the seat pan and activated during the first movement of the seat. After a delay of 1.2sec the central lock opened and released the firing control for the harness; and a manual override was also provided.

To aid separation an apron was also introduced, this being activated by a separate power driven gun soon after the harness was released. Empty weight of this seat rose by 15kg to 30kg in the final design and it could be used from 125m in level flight; the max IAS to ensure fin clearance was 1,000km/hr. As far as is known the Type 29 seat was used on 83 occasions of which 66 were successful, the first recorded incident being on 27 October 1952 and the last on 16 April 1968.

The most important innovation incorporated in the design of the seat for the J32 Lansen was a centrally located firing gun and separate guide rails, which followed the established pattern of British seats. The Lansen was a large two-seat interceptor, strike and reconnaissance aircraft powered by a Rolls-Royce Avon engine. The prototype made its maiden flight on 3 November 1952 and on 25 October 1953 it became the first Swedish-built aircraft to fly faster than sound. In emergency situations the large heavy cockpit was designed to release backwards and rotate on rear-mounted bearings, firing the ejection seats as it went — the Swedish approach was to activate the seats by the action of jettisoning the canopy rather than the reverse as adopted by Martin-Baker. However, this could well have created problems that may have been solved by a sequential ejection sequence but which at that time was some way off. So the original design concept was dropped and removed from aircraft fitted with it, and instructions issued to abandon the aircraft by ejection through the canopy. The seat, which was adjustable in three positions, was fitted with three pairs of guide rollers which, during ejection, ran on rails attached to the airframe. On either side of the headrest there were Plexiglass 'ears' which reduced pitch rotation.

Although also equipped with two explosive charges, the operation was slightly different from British seats. The prime charge was located at the top of the tube and fired mechanically, whereas the secondary was placed lower down and initiated by gases from the upper cartridge. Operation of the seat was by the face screen or seat firing handle. Fitting and release of the harness was in essence the same as that fitted to the later marks of J29 seat, as was the parachute and survival pack. On the Lansen there was no provision for interconnection between the two occupants' seats, and to minimise the risk of collision between the two on ejection, there was a standard instruction that the pilot would eject after his companion. During service, modifications were introduced including an inertia lock to the harness, and replacement of the guide rollers by slide bars which greatly improved the smoothness of acceleration. An automatic parachute release developed by CQ Parachutes Ltd was also brought into service. After a 2sec delay following separation by the automatic apron method, the retaining flaps of the pack opened and the parachute deployed. During high-altitude ejections this release was locked by a barostat which operated at 3,000m while to improve low level performance the harness release time was reduced to 0.4sec. A manual override system was also available. The modifications introduced also saw the first use of CQ's tailor-made 'shaped' canopy, which was designated KFF54. The final change was the replacement of the emergency equipment soft pack by a hard shell, which decreased the acceleration strain experienced by the pilot during the initial ejection sequence.

All these modifications saw the weight of the final design for this seat go up from 40kg to 46kg, and the length of the drogue gun to 1.04m. Maximum speed to ensure clearance of the aircraft's fin was 750km/hr and the minimum altitude at which safe ejection was possible was 50m in level flight, and 1,500m with the aircraft diving vertically. Total production of this seat was 894.

When Saab commenced design of the 105 SK60 side-by-side trainer counter-insurgency aircraft, provision was made for fitting the seat first used on the J29. However, improvements brought about by the introduction of the central firing gun and automatic operation as well as the special need for more in-flight adjustments, saw the development of a completely new low-priced lightweight seat. The Saab 105 made its maiden flight on 29 June 1963 and a total of 150 were ordered by the Swedish Air Force. (As an aside, it is interesting to record that the aircraft's designers saw in their creation the possibility of a high-speed civil aircraft in which the two ejection seats could be replaced by four conventional seats. Although in theory this was a worthwhile move, no civil versions were sold since being a twin-engined aircraft civilian regulations required a two-man crew which reduced its flexibility. Only the military SK60 machine was therefore built and government restrictions on the export of military equipment brought an end to possible overseas sales, although the Austrian government bought 40 of the later 105XT models that were designated 105öE.)

The 105 seats were installed with a backward angle of 19° and inclined outwards at 2°. The seat pan could be continuously adjusted in flight by means of an electrically operated jack, and recommended ejection was through the canopy. In essence all modifications described for the J32 seat were incorporated in the trainer including the hard-pack emergency equipment, and automatic operation. On the versions sold to Austria the automatic release was set to 4,000m instead of 3,000m.

In addition to the Lansen and Type 105, Saab was also very much involved in the possibility of installing ejection seats in another two-seat fighter, the Gloster Meteor NF11. In September 1950, representatives of the Swedish Air Force approached Armstrong Whitworth Aircraft (AWA) and spoke about the possibility of buying Meteor NF11s with DH Goblin engines, fitted with reheat, and equipped with Saab-designed ejection seats. At that time de Havilland was not only supplying Vampires to Sweden but also finalising agreements for licence production of the Goblin and Ghost engines by Svenska/Flygmotor, and it was agreed that there would be no problems in supplying AWA, so design work was started under the supervision of H. Watson of AWA. To accommodate the Saab seats the Meteor's fuselage was lengthened initially by 19.5in, later reduced to 12in by altering the proposed angle of installation in the rear seat. Correspondence between Gen Bengt Jacobsson and AWA indicates that the Swedish Air Force was very much in favour of buying the modified aircraft, but towards the end of 1950 and early 1951 there appears to be some form of outside pressure exerted, because although the enthusiasm of the air force chiefs did not waver, the proposed Meteor acquisition was shelved, and existing records which might explain why are no longer available. It is also interesting that surviving letters and papers also refer to a side-by-side arrangement very much like the eventual 105, but all this is another story which has yet to be revealed. Nevertheless, Saab did come very close to installing seats of its design in a British-built night-fighter, which in the end was never equipped with any type of ejection seat.

Within a year of the J29 making its maiden flight, Saab was already looking at the design of a fighter capable of intercepting bombers flying at Mach 0.9 at an altitude of 36,000ft. In 1949 little was known about supersonic flight and many, including the Royal Institute of Technology in Stockholm, expressed doubts as to the possibility of producing any aircraft able to fly above 500mph; the fighter that evolved from Saab's 1949 design study was the J35 Draken which eventually flew at Mach 2. The team readily admit that having to begin somewhere, they chose the cross-sectional area, reasoning that drag would be critical and thus keeping this to a minimum would bring the target speed within reach. Mathematical analysis also indicated that a double delta wing offered the best configuration for a supersonic aeroplane. A 70% full size test aircraft proved the design and by the time the Draken began to take its final shape, ejection seats were well established. To keep a low frontal area it was necessary to design a completely new seat, and this was later developed into Saab's first rocket-powered ejection seat and gave a ground-level escape capability. The J35, which was the last Saab aircraft to be designed on a conventional drawing board, made its maiden flight on 25 October 1955. When production finally ended 644 machines had been built, and in addition to equipping the Swedish Air Force they had also been supplied to Denmark (52) and Finland, which also built 12 aircraft under licence at the Valmet plant. In 1985 Austria purchased 24 reconditioned J35s.

The seat developed for the first production J35s needed to be compact to keep the frontal area of the aircraft small, but at the same time had to retain the long-stroke ejection gun and be adjustable for pilots of varying heights. This was achieved by making the seat pan adjustable to six different positions within the fixed overall vertical structure. The pan carried a back type parachute and emergency pack, and a dampening device was fitted to cushion the impact in the event of a crash-landing with the seat and occupants still in situ. The headrest, which was movable backwards, contained the firing blind which was also supplemented by the now standard secondary firing lever attached to the lower part of the pan. Harness equipment was virtually the same as that developed for earlier seats, as was the time delay and barostatic control system. Modifications incorporated into the new seat laid the foundations for the introduction of the Saab 35 Draken Rocket Seat Escape System. Major modifications were the removal of the face blind firing screen so that the lower seat pan mechanism became the only activator, a firing handle with double electrical circuits for canopy jettisoning, and the introduction of fully automatic leg restraints, as well as an increase of 50% in the seat ejection cartridge power. Due to the larger canopy of the two-seat J35C it was necessary to introduce a slightly increased time delay to enable the heavier canopy to be carried away, as well as introduce a differential in the two firing mechanisms to prevent collision between the seats. This was done by reducing the rear seat's gun tube by 34mm, making the time delay on firing 1.4sec on the front seat and 0.4sec on the rear.

One of the vital needs for successful low-level ejection is for the seat and occupant to gain sufficient height for the sequence to operate and the personal parachute to deploy fully. Limitations of the human frame prevented what might appear to have been the simple answer of increasing the firing charge, and it was clearly not possible to introduce further progressive acceleration with the cartridge system. The answer was to provide the seat with some form of motive power that would project it safely to a height where the normal sequence would work. This came in the form of a rocket motor attached to the seat and both Martin-Baker and Saab worked towards this aim.

The Saab rocket motor developed for the J35F seat consisted of a cylindrical case with five nozzles along a generatrix across the seat fixed under the pan. The charge was slices of perchlorate powder with a total weight of 2kg. Firing was by pressure originated from the main gun, and burn time, which gave a propulsion of 20kN, was in the order of 0.2sec. With the installation of the rocket motor it was possible to reduce the size of the cartridge charges fitted to the standard gun. A new stabilising parachute was designed for the rocket seats and this was fixed to the back of them.

Total weight of the rocket seat complete with packs was 101kg, an increase of 21kg over the normal seat from which it was developed, and it was eventually fitted to all versions of the J35 including the 35C in which the guide rails were separated outwards from each other to avoid the possibility of collision. This aircraft was also later equipped with a sequential system ensuring that the front seat always fired first independent of which occupant had started the sequence.

The rocket-powered seat was also standard fitting for the J37 Viggen which made its debut in 1967, and was produced in both single and two-seat versions. Both types of seat were of course fully automatic in operation; and service experience and advances in technology led to improvements being added, all of which contributed to saving the lives of aircrew faced with emergency situations at all heights or positions of the aircraft. Decisions to eject had to be made in the knowledge that the safety equipment would not fail them and would operate correctly as they had been assured during training. A typical ejection sequence for the Saab rocket seat would be:

1. Both handles located on either side of the seat are pulled up. As well as starting the sequence, this action also releases the safety covers over the manual override handles.
2. A spring-loaded catch on the firing mechanism is pulled away.
3. Shoulder straps are retracted and locked by a ballistic rotary actuator.
4. The canopy locks are opened by means of electrically-operated ballistic actuators.
5. The canopy raisers lift the canopy which is removed by the slipstream.
6. As the canopy departs it activates the ejection gun.
7. The legs are restrained.
8. Pipes for oxygen and g-suit are disconnected and the valve for the emergency oxygen supply is opened.
9. At speeds over 270kt the time delay for the harness release is switched over.
10. Start of the time delay.
11. The parachute arming wire is locked to the seat.

12. The leg restraint cords start to loosen from their location points with the aircraft.
13. The rocket motor fires.
14. The seat stabiliser parachute gun is actuated by pressure from the seat gun and is fired.
15. The drogue gun pulls out a locking pin in the cover over the stabiliser and pulls out the auxiliary parachute which in turn extracts the stabiliser and retards the seat.
16. The harness is released from the seat.
17. The leg restraint cords are released from the seat.
18. Separation between man and seat occurs.
19. The top of the parachute pack opens and a drogue containing an auxiliary parachute and stabiliser is pulled out.
20. The time delay in the main parachute is armed. (Release time is 0.5sec at an altitude of 10,000ft and lower. Above this it is blocked by the barostat.)
21. The parachutes are immediately released from the stowage and the auxiliary is deployed. (If the descent time to 10,000ft is shorter than the time it takes for the seat to turn into the correct position, then the auxiliary is not released but extracts the main parachute at once.)
22. The stabiliser drogue (or the auxiliary parachute below 10,000ft) is released from the attachment points in the harness.
23. The cover over the main parachute with the auxiliary is opened and the stabiliser starts to extract the main parachute.
24. The life raft cover is opened and the raft is inflated when the crewman starts to free himself from the harness.

In the event of the seat failing to operate when the set procedure is started, several emergency procedures are defined. These include releasing the handles which ensure the harness stays locked, operating the canopy jettison switch or manually jettisoning it, or alternatively operating the override handles and ejecting through the canopy. Manual override systems are provided through every sequence, but such has been the testing of the rocket seats under all conditions that it is very unlikely that any ejectee would ever be faced with a situation in which he would need to carry out all of them. Saab is justifiably proud of the work it has contributed to not only ejection seat design but also flight safety equipment including survival packs, life jackets, anti-g suits and communication equipment. Although its latest design, the JAS39 Gripen, is to be fitted with the Martin-Baker Mk 10L, the advanced technology developed by the company in its first 50 years has placed it among the world's leading and most respected contributors to flight safety equipment, as well as the aircraft in which it has been installed.

Above:
A test shot of a Saab seat from a Saab J32 Lansen. *Saab*

Below and right:
A sequence showing the testing of a rocket seat by Saab. The pictures show the complete sequence from initial firing to parachute deployment. *Saab*

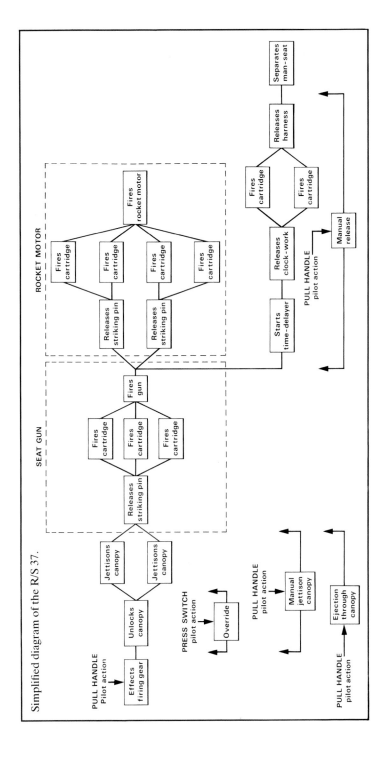

Simplified diagram of the R/S 37.

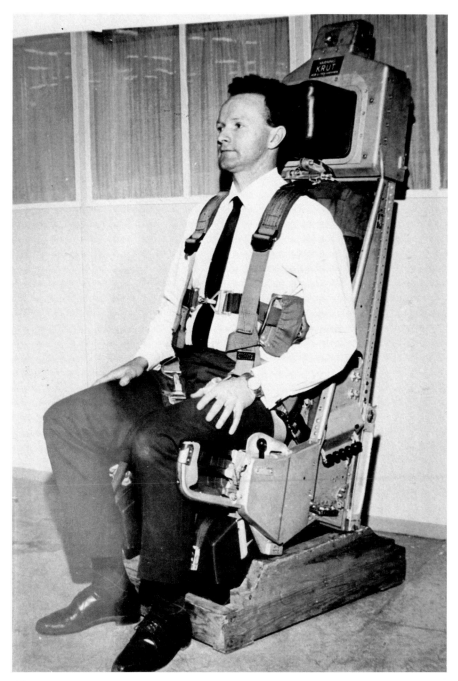

Above:
The Saab rocket seat showing the placement of the pilot's harness. *Saab*

61

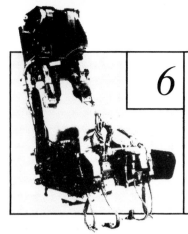

6 A Look At The USA

The end of World War 2 saw the spoils of war divided among the victors. Included were examples of German ejection seats, some of which found their way to the USA where as early as 23 January 1943 a committee had been formed at Wright Field (now Wright Patterson) to study assisted exit from high-speed aircraft, especially those fitted with pusher propellers.

An American study of an early Heinkel seat, filed at the Air Force Central Museum located at Wright Patterson, reveals that it was in fact well aware of the need to get the seat and its occupant away from the aircraft (reference is in fact made to the Ju87) as quickly as possible, after which the urgent requirement was to separate the two. Tests indicate that the Germans controlled the flight of the seat by a drogue which deployed 2sec after ejection. The timer arming mechanism was attached to the aircraft and started it as soon as the ejection sequence was initiated. This activated a ripcord which released the drogue pack by freeing springs which projected the stabilising parachute (or drag chute as it was called) into the slipstream. The seat was therefore prevented from tumbling uncontrollably and allowed to decelerate without applying excessive 'g' forces. It was estimated that with the drogue deployed at sea level a time of 4sec would be ample to attain vertical terminal velocity of 138ft/sec when the ejection took place at speeds approaching 600mph. The German technique of escape from the seat after attaining terminal velocity was by manually releasing the safety belt which included a shoulder harness, then operating a personal parachute in the conventional way. The German seat was much to the forefront in early American experiments although it was never successfully fired in its original form from an American aircraft. It is quite clear from this, and similar analysis in other chapters, that from the very beginning all designers were striving to reach the same goal, which they did, but by different ways and within different time envelopes.

Unlike the situation in Europe, where both manufacture and design was mostly undertaken by one company within each country, in the USA many aircraft and safety equipment manufacturers turned their attention to ejection seats, and the opinion has often been expressed that the resulting multiplicity hindered rather than helped development, causing the USAF in particular many problems. Since the objective of all seats was the same, and in one way or another this was met, there is little point in a detailed account of each manufacturer's approach, so it is perhaps better to concentrate on areas where the Americans gave more attention than other companies.

North American, Lockheed, Grumman, Republic, Douglas and Stencel all produced ejection seats, which in most cases were fitted to aircraft of their design. American designers opted for initiating the firing sequence by levers located in the armrests, or in some cases by pulling up the complete armrests. Problems identical to those encountered in Germany, England and Sweden were of course met and overcome, although the introduction of leg restraints, correct separation sequence, totally automatic separation and so on were much slower to be incorporated. The first American live ejection was by 1Sgt Larry Lambert from a modified P-61 on 17 August 1946.

In contrast, introduction of early seats into service was faster than it had been in Britain, but there was also a marked reluctance on the part of aircrew to view the seat with any great confidence. In a bid to overcome this the ejection seat was 'sold' to aircrew by a series of live demonstrations at selected venues by former bomber pilot Capt Vince Mazza. The first of these took place over San Pablo Bay from a F-80 flying at 10,000ft and travelling at over 500mph. If any further convincing was needed it came later the same year in South Carolina when the pilot of a F2H-1 had a genuine emergency and ejected safely at 597mph.

Many lessons were learned from the Korean War which gave the Americans an ideal opportunity to assess the ejection seat under combat conditions. The USAF investigated 1,928 Korean ejections and found that 69% of the users had experienced no difficulties. The remaining 31% had problems ranging from reaching triggers, releasing canopies, slipstream, actuating the seat, ejecting through the canopy, premature seat operation, hitting the canopy before it had released fully, injuries because the body or limbs had been in incorrect positions for ejection, failure to remove safety locking pins, and so on. Navy pilots, especially those forced to eject at low level and in some cases soon after launch from their carriers, reported severe tumbling, high acceleration and air blasts that made it impossible for them to release themselves from their seats quickly. Some also reported that they were so confused that they pulled the parachute ripcord before releasing the seat harness. Others estimated that it took between 5sec to 20sec to release themselves from the seat after ejection. There were also the usual stories of ejection at too low a level for the seat to operate, problems occurring at high altitude due to the shock of the parachute opening as the pilot fell too fast, and oxygen starvation and frostbite, as well as pilots being killed because comparatively minor arm injuries prevented them from carrying out vital actions, and all gave food for thought. Most of the problems were encountered by variations of the methods described elsewhere, but study of contemporary documents does suggest that due to the variety of designs then being used within American aircraft, some were not introduced as quickly as they might have been.

National pride perhaps dictated that every consideration should be given to American-designed and manufactured ejection seats. Early on the US Navy showed a preference for the Martin-Baker method, although the Air Force was quite adamant that it preferred American seats. The situation was not helped when Navy chiefs insisted that they needed a seat with a very low-level capability whilst the USAF considered that any ejection below 500ft (at that time) was outside the survival envelope it was interested in. Grumman was far from happy when the Navy requested a Cougar be made available for tests of the Martin-Baker seat, but when an 'either or' ultimatum was issued the company gave in, although still worried about its reputation if a fatality occurred. As will be seen in the next chapter the Martin-Baker/Grumman tests were successful and a long-lasting relationship with the US Navy was established.

This antagonised the US companies then manufacturing ejection seats. Douglas' Escapac seat was probably the most successful and had a performance very close to that of Martin-Baker's, although it was not until the mid-1970s that it incorporated many features that had long been standard on British seats. During 1960-66 the average fatality rate for non-combat USAF ejections was 16%, ranging from a low of 14% to a high of 19%. From 1970-73 the rate increased to 47%, 1974-77 to 53% and 1978-81 to 59%, the alarming escalation being due to an increasing switch to operational low-level tactics as well as including figures for ejections below 500ft. These figures could well have been higher if it had not been for Escapac and M-B seats, as highlighted in a 1982 report. The same report however also pointed a somewhat accusing finger at both seats for the high fatality rate; very much a 'heads I win, tails you lose' situation.

Turning back the clock to 1957, the Wright Patterson Air Development Center (WADC) abandoned its studies into ground-level ejection because it felt that the catapult forces needed to lift the seat and occupant high enough for full parachute deployment were far too high and would always result in spinal injuries. At this time the USAF was testing the same catapult unit as that installed in the Navy's F-94, but it would just not operate successfully in the Century series of fighters. The USAF stipulated a maximum vertical acceleration limit of 22g, whereas the M-B seats then on test were between 32.2g and 32.5g. These were figures that WADC did not like and so it decided to seek alternatives. The USAF goal was 12g, which it achieved with some seats providing the pilot ejected above 500ft.

This height was not acceptable to the Navy so it looked at means of improving what was then available. Studies indicated that a force of 200lb/sq in was required to get the seat clear of the airframe in one action. Using the 40in stroke gun fitted to the seat under test, and equipping it with a solid $2\frac{1}{2}$in $\times$ 1in 'charge' shaped into a rod with seven vertical holes for flame propagation, failed to achieve the result the Navy wanted. BuAir requested BuWeps to develop a rocket motor to improve the capability of American design seats, and it was at this point that 'politics' began to take a prominent part. After the US Navy developed the Rocket Catapult, known as RAPEC — Rocket Assist Personnel Ejection Catapult — the Patuxent River tests with the Martin-Baker seat went ahead. Vought and Douglas were experimenting with rocket-powered seats, and both had units capable of use at 100kt at 150ft. They were based on a lightweight seat built at the request of Ed Heinemann for his A-4 fighter, so it was not too surprising that LTV which built the aircraft desperately wanted to install its seat in those supplied to the Navy. In a no-holds-barred situation the decision eventually went in favour of Douglas whose Escapac RAPEC seat was specified for the A-4 with Martin-Baker getting the rest of the Navy's requirements, which included the LTV F8 Crusader in which the LTV seat was replaced by the British-built unit. In another twist to the tale, North American Aviation was allowed to produce its own seats for the A-5 and T-2. In a parallel programme an uprated RAPEC seat, manufactured by Stanley Aviation Inc, was installed in the Martin P6M as the originals had insufficient power to clear the aircraft's high 'T' tailplane.

The uprated RAPEC rocket had a polysulfide propellant base developed by Thikol Chemical Corporation. This was wrapped in a Talco case and retrofitted to the P6M seats, providing an average thrust of 3,000lb and a peak of 4,600lb at lift-off. Measurements during test when the seat was carrying a 200lb instrumented dummy indicated a peak 17-18g at the pelvis. The trajectory of the seat at Mach 0.961 was about 50ft above the P6M tail, which meant that at 120kt it went almost 200ft into the air. When the first P6M crashed the results with the normal ballistic seats were not good, but when the second nosed over at Mach 0.75 and the wings folded, every crew member escaped with the aid of the rocket seat.

The American experiments with rocket-powered seats were conducted in August-November 1957, and the BuAir manager Bill Thomas attempted to get Martin-Baker interested. At that time James Martin was occupied with other developments, but he was aware of the need for such a development and it did of course come about, as we shall see later.

The T-2J and A-5 Vigilante were perhaps the most successful aircraft in terms of escape survivability with the rocket-powered seat. On 5 September 1963, A-5 BuNo 148930 was at 10,000ft travelling at between Mach 0.95 and Mach 1.03 when it started to roll to the right and the nose dropped by 60°. The crew ejected, the navigator leaving at Mach 0.95 and the pilot at Mach 1.03. The former suffered a fatal neck injury (possibly caused by aerodynamic forces), but the pilot was uninjured. There was a happier outcome on 19 August 1966 when the crew of another A-5, BuNo 149309, used their seats with the aircraft inverted at 2,000ft travelling at 550kt, both men survived with no injuries.

In Vietnam the RA-5 was used for both pre and post-strike reconnaissance, the crews taking their aircraft in low and fast where they were vulnerable to ground fire and missiles. It was reassuring to know that the chances of escape even at high speed were good: in fact over 25% of all RA-5 combat ejections in Vietnam were above Mach 1.00. The HS-1 seat fitted to this aircraft was the only zero/zero-to-700kt open-type seat produced by an American manufacturer, and when the RA-5 was withdrawn from service, so too went the only open seat with a truly Mach 1-plus recovery. But it did lay the foundations for the CREST programme currently being worked on by Boeing.

This will be an open seat with zero/zero-to-70,000ft and 700kt to Mach 3.00 capability, with an adverse flight configuration low of 100ft. The CREST rocket system will consist of six to eight propellant cans with some 60lb of charge. The twin omni-axial thrust vector nozzles will direct the seat via computer control to effect a survivable ejection. Structured in three phases, the CREST programme will seek to provide protection for aircrews during flight manoeuvres as well as after ejection. A need exists for the seat to have special aircrew protection as USAF requirements demand future aircraft to fly at greater speeds both at high and low altitudes. Current military machines such as the A-10, F-15 and F-16 are all equipped with the Advanced Concept Ejection Seat II (ACES II) which has lessened the injuries and fatalities during ejections when compared to older designs. Future fighters, however, will be required to fly radically different manoeuvres, such as sideward acceleration which was not envisaged when the ACES II seat was designed.

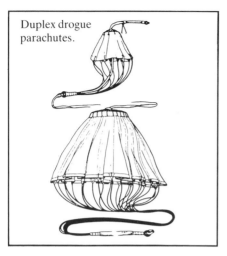

Duplex drogue parachutes.

Right:
Larry Lambert after landing from the first live ejection in the USA on 17 August 1946. *USAF*

Below:
The camera catches (just!) Sgt Lambert ejecting from the P-61 *Jack-in-the-Box* on 17 August 1946. *USAF*

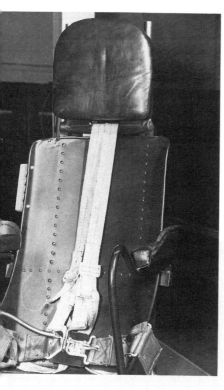

Left:
An early Lockheed seat from an F-80
Shooting Star. *USAF*

Below:
A Republic seat similar to the type used by
Flt Lt John West when he ejected from a
RF-84F. *Bryan Wilburn*

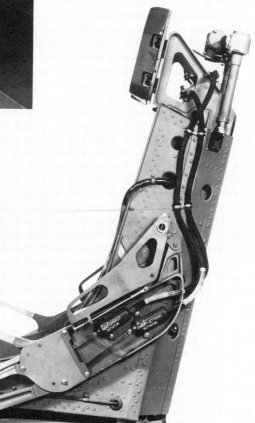

The CREST seat will also provide better restraint, increased wind-blast protection, permit varied control of thrust after ejection, use digital flight control electronics for seat stability and steering, and incorporate sensing of the aircraft's speed, altitude and attitude independent from the aircraft's sensing system. It will also include advanced technologies addressing multiple rocket propulsion with selectable thrust and attitude control for the optimum safe ejection speed and trajectory. The seat may also be able to be modified for multiple escape systems, for more than one aircrew member where trajectory steering would avoid collision during multiple simultaneous escapes. A final aim is to make the seat easily removable from the airframe for servicing even under front-line combat environments. Engineering development is expected to be complete by April 1989 and production planned for 1994 or 1995.

One of the most distinguished users of an early rocket-powered seat was the first man to fly faster than sound, Gen Charles (Chuck) Yeager, who on 12 December 1963 saved his life when the specially equipped NF-104 he was flying went out of control after a zoom climb to 104,000ft. Yeager's own graphic account of this and the injuries he suffered when he was hit by the seat after separation are related in his book *Yeager*, published in 1986 by Century Hutchinson Ltd.

A less famous but equally grateful pilot who used a standard Republic-built seat on 7 January 1957 and proved that flailing limbs was not the sole prerogative of Saab or Martin-Baker, was RAF officer Flt Lt John West who at the time was an exchange pilot on the 18th TRS, 363rd TRW, flying a RF-84F Thunderflash aircraft from Shaw AFB, South Carolina. He tells his own tale in the following account:

'I was leading my No 2 — 2Lt Charles Lustig — at about 15,000ft when in a right-hand turn there was a loud bang and the aircraft shook. I thought the No 2 had collided with me and called "are you all right Chuck". He said "yes . . . but you're not, you're on fire".

'It seems that flames had shot out of the jet pipe but soon died out and there was no further evidence of fire — only a thick stream of grey smoke which I could see in my mirror. The engine had quickly run down and seized — as the controls were powered with no manual reversion, there was no chance of a forced landing even had a suitable airfield been available, so I prepared to eject. Ejection in the Republic seat was by two handles on the right armrest. Raising the first handle shattered the retaining bolts on the canopy which was thereupon jettisoned and "cocked" the second handle to which access was available only after the first had been raised. On pulling the second handle, the seat fired and once out of the aircraft, began to tumble in a most alarming fashion. It did not possess the advantage of an ejection apron to which one's hands could cling and Chuck told me later that it was very comical to see me tumbling in the seat with arms and legs flailing everywhere. It wasn't so amusing for me because the disorientation was such that I could not think of anything except that I wanted the motion to stop. Fortunately the seat did have an automatic harness release so I was flung out of it and then fell freely. The parachute opened and I found myself drifting backwards, so I pulled two lift webs across each other to turn myself around.

'However the webs on this particular American 'chute parted at the shoulder and I pulled the wrong ones, partially collapsing the canopy and increasing my rate of descent. Although I was still going backwards I decided to leave things well alone and eventually came to rest in the top of a tall pine. I undid the harness and shinned down the tree to the ground where some loggers gave me a lift to the road. I was eventually picked up by the Air Police from Charleston Air Force Base who thought that I was part of their own base aircrew escape and evasion exercise which was going on at that time. Despite my protestations and the funny accent, which they deemed to be highly suspicious, I was taken to the police cells and held for a couple of hours until Shaw AFB was able to persuade them to release me. I was then flown back to base in a helicopter where we had quite a party. There was no question of a medical checkup.'

The fact that no restraints were fitted and the seat had no drogue to stabilise it is graphically illustrated, and John West was lucky not to suffer serious injuries. In particular the tumbling not only created disorientation but also caused the parachute to snag on the pilot's helmet as it was extracted: the force of this could have broken his neck, but fortunately it was only a slight snag which removed a small piece from the canopy.

Although automatic limb restraint and body harnesses followed a similar if somewhat slower path in America than they did in England, the Americans did investigate other areas at a quicker pace. These included downward ejection, and complete capsules that were of course closely related to the space programme. Because of the unusually high tail surfaces, exceptionally high speeds and the possibility of multiple ejections, a downward-firing seat was an attractive option. The possibility of clearing the high tails of aircraft like the B-47, B-52, B-66 and F-104 with standard ejection guns was extremely unlikely. The 80ft/sec gun solved the problem in England but in America downward ejection was favoured, probably due to the nervousness of the USAF in realistically facing the difficulties it imagined would occur with the human body if the power of the gun adopted was increased. It goes without saying that there was little to recommend downward ejection at low level, but as we already know the space below 1,000ft was generally considered by USAF chiefs to be a non-survivable area in any case. As far as multi-crew bomber aircraft were concerned there was of course much in favour of the downward-firing seat as it did permit multiple crew ejection without a high risk of collision. The first scheme investigated for the B-47 was for the navigator, who was located within the belly of the aircraft, to bale out through a special door in the conventional way whilst the other two crew members had ejection seats and delayed their use long enough for their colleague to leave the aircraft (shades of the British V-bombers). But the idea of providing a downward seat gradually took root and was approved for development at WADC in 1952. On 7 December 1953, Col A. M. (Chic) Henderson tested the seat and became the first man to safely eject downwards from an aircraft in flight, in B-47 coded 052 flown by Capt Bill Campbell with Capt Ralph Lusk as his co-pilot.

The aircraft took off from Elgin AFB, Florida, and after a climb to 10,000ft the Colonel, who was wearing a T1 partial pressure suit, a pressure helmet, lightweight overalls, heavy duty jump boots, a standard back type parachute and a seat parachute as a reserve, ejected at an IAS of 200kt. The result was successful in every aspect and altogether Col Henderson plus Capt Ed Sperry, Lt Hank Nielsen and MSgt George Post made a total of seven live test ejections without major problems, although Post, Sperry and Nielsen during tests 2, 6 and 7 did encounter slight difficulties with the usual problem of the period — flailing limbs. As a result of these tests, modifications to the seat and parachute release were introduced, and on 9 July 1954, Col Henderson made the first of a new series of ejections during which the speed was progressively increased from 300kt to 425kt. After the 9 July test the Colonel described the moment immediately after leaving the B-47 as being 'like a Saint Bernard dog shaking a rabbit in its mouth'. The series proved successful and there were no further problems with the parachute 'D' ring or flailing legs, so the downward seat was approved and entered service — although perhaps rather predictably it did not remain too long in the F-104.

As early as 1946 one school of thought in America believed that the future for high-altitude, high-speed escape systems lay with a completely closed capsule and not an open type seat. At sea level air pressure is about 14lb/sq in, at 18,000ft it is half of that and at 34,000ft it is half again. Above 50,000ft a man cannot breathe unless he is in a pressurised cabin or suit because the pressure in the lungs is equal to the pressure of oxygen trying to get into them. Above 60,000ft, the air pressure is so low that body fluids will seep out through the pores of the skin and evaporate or simply boil away. Uncontrolled tumbling produces gas expansion, ear blockages and the much feared 'bends', so there were many arguments in favour of a module that was ejected in total from the aircraft. Such a module was of course a vital element for escape from spacecraft, which is a separate subject and outside an in-depth study in this book.

Once again it has to be said that nothing is new, and the first workable system in which the whole cockpit area was jettisoned was designed by the Germans and fitted to the Heinkel He176. The F-111 is perhaps the best known example of an aircraft with a complete modular escape system and is described in the story 'It Worked As Advertised', in the second part of this book. The Stanley Aviation Corporation produced an individual escape capsule which was used, albeit with a relatively high failure rate, on the B-58 Hustler. On initiation, the Encapsulated Seat System (to give it its proper title) retracted both body and legs, closed the lobster-like door and pressurised the capsule. On ejection the crewman remained inside for the total descent. When it was deployed, the recovery parachute was held in a half-open position for 2sec to reduce opening shock. After this, cutters severed the reefing line thus allowing the 41ft diameter ring-sail parachute to blossom fully. Ground impact force was reduced by crushable cylinders attached to the back of the capsule, while four flotation outriggers with bags attached maintained stability in the event of ejection into water. (The capsule was in fact designed to float without the aid of the bags, which were simply to stabilise it.)

Once on the ground or in the water, the internal environment of the 57lb capsule greatly assisted survival. First live tests of the system were carried out by Chief Warrant Officer Ed Murray who ejected in one at 20,000ft and simply commented 'No sweat' when he landed and was greeted by medical experts and the capsule's designers.

Testing of similar systems using bears and other animals which have body structures similar to man's is continuing, with speeds of Mach 1.6 and heights above 45,000ft in sight. The capsule used in the B-70 was the only one to have been fully flight tested and approved before the prototype aircraft had actually flown.

The Stanley Corporation also came up with another unique idea designed for use in aircraft where it was impossible to retrospectively fit ejection seats. Known as 'Yankee' this consisted basically of a tractor rocket attached to the pilot's torso harness. When the rocket was launched, the seat pan folded down and was disconnected from the seat back which remained with the extracted occupant. Just before 'burn-out', an integral sensor separated the man from the rocket while a drogue assisted in the deployment of the quick-opening parachute, which was forcibly spread ballistically by a second small rocket. The device was fitted to some aircraft including the A-1 Skyraider, and it was from such an aircraft that Maj James E. Holler became the first to use it. Maj Holler was taking off from Pleiku AFB for a combat sortie in Vietnam when the engine of his aircraft lost power. Being far too low to bale out in the conventional manner he used the Yankee system and landed safely in nearby scrubland, breaking both ankles. Maj Holler weighed over 200lb and later commented to other pilots, 'If the system works on this bulk of mine, then it will work on anyone'. It is interesting that at the time of this incident (1967) the Stanley extraction system provided a zero/zero capability which was not then available in conventional in-service ejection seats.

Experiences in Vietnam led to the investigation of two other devices to help aircrew survival. Karman Aircraft worked on a rescue seat called SAVER (Stowable Aircrew Vehicle Escape Rotoseat). This was an ejection seat powered by a 275lb thrust turbofan equipped with stowable telescopic blades, with the turbofan and controls, stowed into the seat. Following ejection, the folded rotor opened, the engine started, and the seat became a gyroplane. The aim was to achieve a range of 50 miles and a speed of 100kt, but the device was not taken beyond the early design stage due to technical difficulties and the end of the Vietnam War.

The PARD (Pilot Airborne Recovery Device) developed by Goodyear Aerospace Corporation was another attempt to enable aircrew who ejected over enemy territory to reach the safety of their own lines. The aim was two-fold — firstly to enable the ejected airman to remain bouyant for 30min outside the range of small arms fire, and second to be rescued from the air. After normal ejection and at terminal velocity in his parachute, the ram-air-filled Ballute (a large balloon-shaped parachute) was deployed above the conventional one. At a predetermined time, a butane burner ignited and with an initial burn rate the system became buoyant. A lower sustaining burn rate held the altitude and the occupant could ascend or descend by operating a fuel flow control valve. In tests at Luke AFB, Arizona, a float time of 30min was demonstrated using a wide range of different weight aircrew. The system was compatible with the Martin-Baker Mk 7 seat, and an aircraft-mounted pick-up system was devised for use on rescue aircraft, to absorb the pick-up energy and retrieve the ejectee. The primary functions of the system were to engage the device and accelerate the person being rescued to aircraft velocity without exceeding allowable 'g' loads. Mid-air retrieval, tow and (later) safe re-inflation of the Ballute was successfully demonstrated with a C-130 at the Parachute Test Facility, El Centre, California, but it seems likely that once again the end of the war in Vietnam brought development to a close.

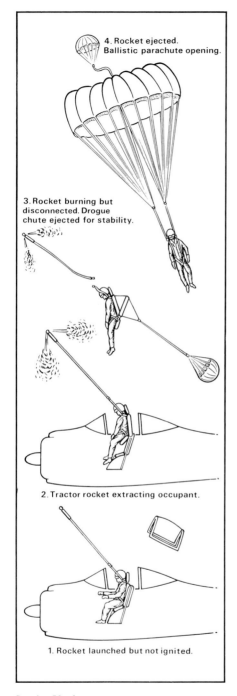

4. Rocket ejected. Ballistic parachute opening.

3. Rocket burning but disconnected. Drogue chute ejected for stability.

2. Tractor rocket extracting occupant.

1. Rocket launched but not ignited.

Stanley Yankee system.

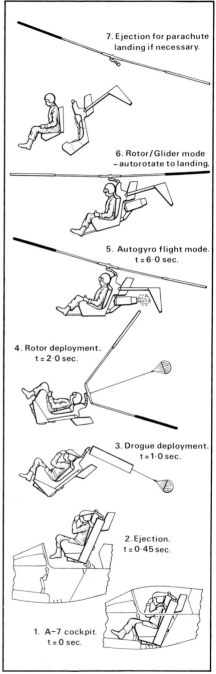

7. Ejection for parachute landing if necessary.

6. Rotor/Glider mode – autorotate to landing.

5. Autogyro flight mode. t = 6·0 sec.

4. Rotor deployment. t = 2·0 sec.

3. Drogue deployment. t = 1·0 sec.

2. Ejection. t = 0·45 sec.

1. A-7 cockpit. t = 0 sec.

Karman Saver Rotoseat.

 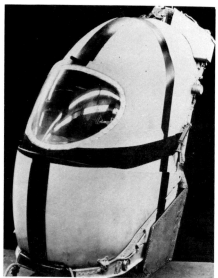

Above:
The Stanley capsule installed in the bombardier and navigator's positions in the B-58. The front closes like a clamshell just prior to ejection. *Bryan Wilburn*

Above right:
The Stanley escape capsule in the closed position. This particular example was used for tests from a rocket sled. *Bryan Wilburn*

Below and overleaf:
Mk 4 Martin-Baker seat: sequential diagrams to show its operation.

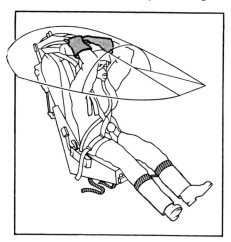 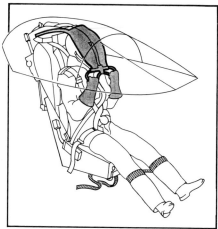

Preparing to eject.

Face screen pulled to commence ejection sequence.

Canopy jettisoned.

Action of leg restraints.

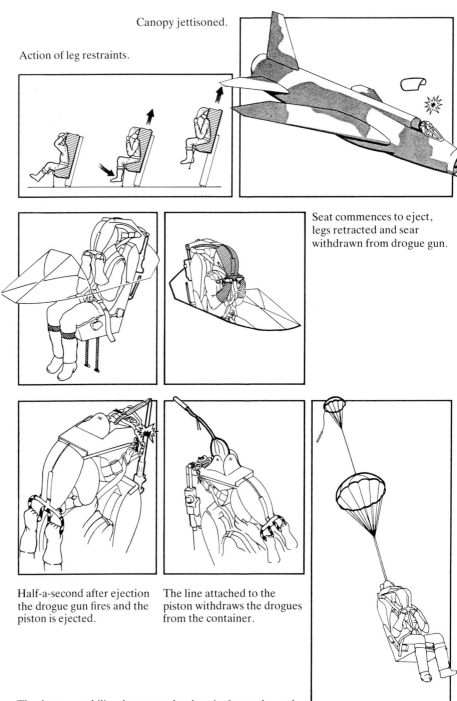

Seat commences to eject, legs retracted and sear withdrawn from drogue gun.

Half-a-second after ejection the drogue gun fires and the piston is ejected.

The line attached to the piston withdraws the drogues from the container.

The drogues stabilise the seat and reduce its forward speed.

74

When the seat is below
10,000ft and the speed has
reduced sufficiently, the time
release unit operates and the
scissor shackle opens.

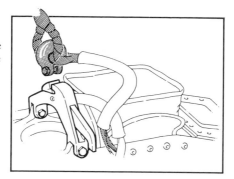

The pull of the drogues is
transferred to the lifting lines
and the face screen and
parachute and the occupant is
lifted out of the seat, allowing
the seat to fall free.

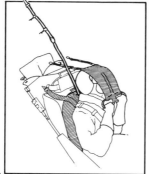

The occupant makes a
normal parachute descent.

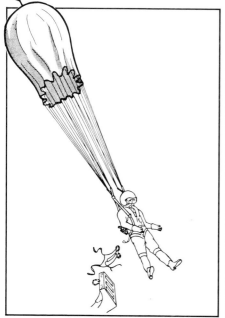

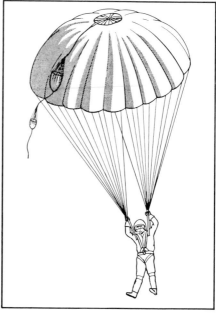

7 Back To Britain

Although the name Martin-Baker is now synonymous with ejection seats in England and it rightly holds the premier position in research and design, two other British companies did for a short while compete with it. In the late 1940s and early 1950s ML Aviation produced a seat designed by Marcel Lobelle, a Belgian who for many years was the Chief Designer of Fairey Aviation. Among the aircraft for which he was responsible were the Swordfish and Fairey Fox. The first seats designed by the company were fitted with a 60ft/sec gun and were not automatic in operation. In 1951 the Mks 3 and 4, which were automatic and had 80ft/sec guns, were produced, but as far as it is possible to ascertain were never fitted into aircraft. The earlier seat, however, was experimentally fitted into a Meteor and Wyvern as well as the experimental Hawker 1081 (VX279). This aircraft was a modified version of the 1052 which was basically a swept-wing version of the Sea Hawk. The modified aircraft was powered by a Rolls-Royce Nene engine exhausting through a conventional tail pipe instead of the split pipes exiting aft of the wing roots. The 1081 was later modified to investigate boundary layer control and was fitted with wing boundary layer fences. On 3 April 1951 the aircraft was lost in a crash and popular Hawker test pilot Sqn Ldr Trevor (Wimpey) Wade was killed. In aviation circles there was a suggestion that there was a malfunction of the ML seat, and soon afterwards the company ceased producing ejection seats. It did however continue making associated aviation equipment, as well as carrying out sub-contract work for Folland Aircraft. Unfortunately ML declined to answer correspondence so it is not possible to outline their seats in greater detail.

Manufacturing rights for the Saab Mk 2 seat as installed in the J29 were acquired by the Folland Aircraft Co Ltd, which carried out modifications including the provision of automatic release before fitting it into the Gnat lightweight fighter. These two companies were the only British concerns to offer any competition to Martin-Baker, but Folland's interest was confined only to a lightweight seat and by the mid-1950s Martin-Baker became, and remains, the sole British manufacturer of ejection seats. As such it too had to look towards a lighter seat for the new lightweight and less sophisticated fighters that it was believed would be needed to curtail escalating costs of modern jet fighters. The fact that the 1950s concept made no progress beyond the Gnat, a very successful trainer but used only by the Indian Air Force as a fighter, is not part of the present story, which continues with the Martin-Baker Mk 4 seat.

In designing a lightweight seat it was essential that the weight reduction did not impair operational efficiency, so the Mk 4 therefore retained the essential components of its predecessors but at the same time included many new improvements. The basic 80ft/sec ejection gun and duplex drogue were of course essential, but the conventional type of guide rail was eliminated and replaced by channel members mounted on the sides of the ejection gun. Steel slipper pads, mounted on the seat beams, located the seat in position in these channels and guided it out of the aircraft. The total structure was a framework of two side beams bridged by three cross-members, this supporting the seat pan and drogue container; the drogue gun and time-release unit were mounted on the side beams.

The top beam took the full thrust of the ejection gun and contained the seat latch mechanism for locking the seat to the gun. Attachment for the shoulder harness was to the centre cross-member and anchorage for the seat height adjustment was provided by the lower beam. Feedback from users of earlier seats clearly indicated that reaching the head-box-mounted firing handle did prove difficult under certain conditions, so an alternative firing handle was fitted in the leading edge of the pan, which enabled the occupant to eject when adverse 'g' prevented use of the face-screen handle.

Naturally provision of two handles led to much conjecture as to whether or not the lower one should be regarded as the second choice, and in the years before the face screen was finally discarded, there was argument as to which one it was best to use in a variety of situations. Comfort of the seat was improved by the redesign of the parachute and dinghy packs, rather than try to improvise by fitting existing designs into the new seat. The parachute pack was of the back type, horseshoe in shape and mounted high on the seat in an ideal position for automatic deployment. The harness was also redesigned to combine the safety harness so that both formed an all-in-one fitting (with just one quick-release box), fastened during initial strapping in and remaining fastened throughout any subsequent ejection, released only by the occupant at the end of the parachute descent. This combined harness was attached to the seat by two locks in the rear of the pan, and another in the seat at shoulder height. The locks were released through a linkage system by a new TRU at the right instant after ejection. They were also provided with a manual override should the TRU malfunction. This greatly improved combined harness and seat pan firing handle was retrospectively fitted to some Mk 3 seats.

Later Mk 4 seats were fitted with a snubbing unit in the top lock and a release lever which enabled the crew member freedom to lean forward but ensured that he was locked firmly into place in the event of ejection or a crash-landing. A number of different survival packs were designed by Martin-Baker as dictated by customer requirements, but in every case they embodied the principle of seat cushion and container for dinghy and survival equipment. The cushion was designed to give maximum comfort and was filled with a resilient padding slow to return to its original shape, thereby helping to absorb acceleration forces present during ejection. The success of the Mk 4 seat is illustrated by its use in 35 different type of aircraft, the first emergency use being from a Fiat G91 in March 1957.

Another innovation introduced in the Mk 4 was the incorporation of a 'g' switch, to enable high-speed ejections to take place without damage to the main parachute canopy. At low speed, providing the ejection took place below

10,000ft, when the barostat was inoperative, the timer ran unimpeded and released the drogues after 1½sec. In the case of a high-speed ejection, the 'g' switch engaged and a delay in accordance with the deceleration load imposed was automatically selected. The introduction of this switch made it possible to provide for safe ejection at all speeds likely to be encountered by aircraft in service at that time. Later on the delay was reduced by another ¼sec and the 1¼sec time delay unit became standard equipment on the majority of Martin-Baker seats.

To reduce the number of operations needed when making a manual separation after ejection, a guillotine system of disconnecting the parachute withdrawal line from the drogue was introduced. In this a small guillotine unit was mounted, usually on the side of the drogue container, with the parachute withdrawal line positioned in a spring-loaded guard immediately above the cutter blade. A short static line between the back of the parachute case and the sear of the guillotine firing unit was activated by a cartridge. As the occupant moved forward on separation, taking his parachute pack with him, the static line removed the sear to fire the guillotine and cut the withdrawal line. This made the need for two 'D' rings on the parachute harness unnecessary. Should the TRU fail, all that was necessary was for the ejectee to operate the harness release and pull his ripcord to deploy the parachute. A later modification once again reduced the vital time element, by interconnecting the firing of the guillotine with the operation of the manual separation handle instead of using a static line attached to the parachute pack. Other improvements introduced on the Mk 4 included the adoption of leg restraint lines which plugged into latch boxes on the front of the seat pan instead of being secured to the harness release locks at the rear. The 1sec time-delay mechanism after canopy ejection was incorporated into the breech of the main gun, whilst the canopy locks were operated by expanding gases of the canopy jettison charge via a bypass valve instead of the initial movement of the jacks.

The Mk 4 seat proved to be extremely successful and popular with crews, for it introduced more comfort and a better escape envelope ranging across wider speed and altitudes. Among the men who can vouch for the performance of the Mk 4 MSA seat is Lt-Cdr John Eatwell RN (retd), an Observer who used one from a Buccaneer S1 on 8 August 1966: this is his story.

No 736 Naval Air Squadron was the Buccaneer Operational Conversion Unit (OCU) based at RNAS Lossiemouth, and in 1966 was equipped with Buccaneer S1 aircraft. The students were either experienced aircrew converting to the aircraft or those direct from the Advanced Flying School at Brawdy and the Observer School at Lossiemouth.

On the occasions that an aircraft carrier was exercising in the Moray Firth, every effort was made to gain some deck landing practice (DLP) for the students before they joined front-line squadrons. Such sessions were very limited, precisely timed and of short duration. The Staff Observers used to occupy the rear seat on all these DLP sessions, Staff Pilots preferring to confine themselves to the briefing and de-briefing!

On the day in question HMS *Ark Royal* was working up in the Firth and DLP slots were made available to the OCU throughout the day. Each student pilot had completed the required number of mirror-assisted dummy deck landings (MADDLS) and was fully prepared for the big day which would be the culmination of several years of extensive training.

Unfortunately aircraft do not always behave themselves on important occasions and throughout the morning Lt Eatwell and his pilot had manned up for each designated DLP slot only to dismount due to unserviceability of their Buccaneer. The pressure was now on, time was running out, tempers were somewhat short and a considerable degree of frustration was evident. As so often happens on such occasions, everything suddenly changed for the good. Aircraft XN928 became serviceable and a new slot was allocated. The only problem was that Lt Eatwell could not now find his own navigation bag, which had been 'borrowed', so in the confusion he took the first one to hand which happened to belong to the Senior Observer.

On arrival at the carrier the Buccaneer joined the other squadron aircraft already in the pattern. The first approach was slightly tight so an overshoot was made; there was now only 10min remaining as the *Ark* was running out of sea room. The second approach was going well until at 400ft, halfway round the final turn, a tremendous thumping was felt from the port engine. This was caused by the inlet guide vanes (IGV) slamming shut thus stalling the engine. In the landing configuration with 'blow' on and effectively single-engined, the Buccaneer could not be recovered from a height of only 400ft. A rapid uncontrolled roll followed which left only one option . . . ejection.

Lt Eatwell's ejection was almost copy book. He pulled the face blind and went through the canopy with the aircraft in about a 90° bank. He was very much aware of the tremendous acceleration, as well as a thump and a pain between his shoulder blades — this was later found to be a compression fracture of the vertebra T6. After some violent tumbling he suddenly found himself floating in space and can remember seeing the *Ark* steaming away from him as though it were in a picture. This lasted for only a few seconds before the sea rushed up and hit him with a force far greater than he ever imagined. Easily releasing the parachute harness, he pulled the handle to inflate his life jacket . . . there was a loud hiss of gas which unfortunately vented into the atmosphere instead of the buoyancy stole. At this stage things started to get out of hand.

He was badly winded by the ejection and impact and was gasping for breath: thus there was none to spare for oral inflation of the life jacket and he was in grave danger of drowning. However, the repeated and often tiresomely-viewed practice drills undertaken by all RN aircrew paid off. Without really thinking too much about it, he followed the procedure automatically and suddenly his life raft appeared fully inflated in front of him, and this supplied the buoyancy he so desperately needed. The SAR helicopter arrived overhead and the strop was lowered, but in his winded state he was not able to get into it without assistance. As his predicament did not seem to be too bad at that time, the helicopter crew decided to leave him for the time being to help the pilot who was being supported in the water by the SAR diver. The pilot was in fact unconscious as he had left his ejection very late, not leaving the aircraft until it had completed another roll after Lt Eatwell's departure, and he had not achieved a fully stabilised descent before hitting the water. The helicopter and its crew managed to recover both the diver and injured pilot and then returned for the observer.

By this time Lt Eatwell was sufficiently recovered to get into the strop and was winched up to rejoin his pilot aboard the helicopter. A few minutes later they arrived aboard the carrier, but not quite as briefed. Due to the angle he had been

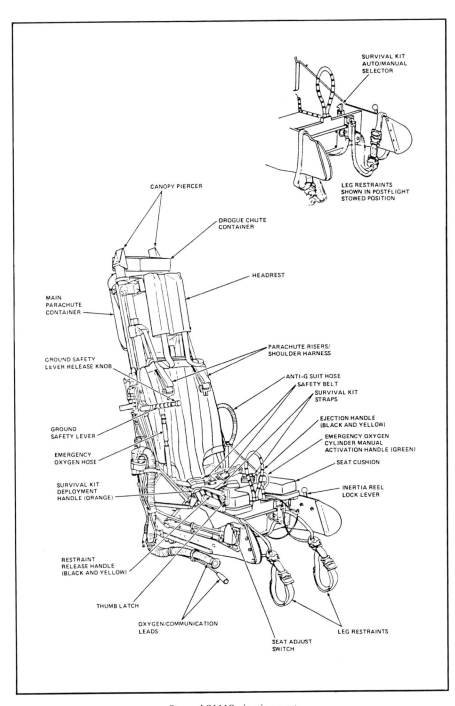

SURVIVAL KIT
AUTO/MANUAL
SELECTOR

CANOPY PIERCER

LEG RESTRAINTS
SHOWN IN POSTFLIGHT
STOWED POSITION

DROGUE CHUTE
CONTAINER

HEADREST

MAIN
PARACHUTE
CONTAINER

PARACHUTE RISERS/
SHOULDER HARNESS

GROUND SAFETY
LEVER RELEASE KNOB

ANTI-G SUIT HOSE
SAFETY BELT
SURVIVAL KIT
STRAPS

EJECTION HANDLE
(BLACK AND YELLOW)

GROUND
SAFETY LEVER

EMERGENCY OXYGEN
CYLINDER MANUAL
ACTIVATION HANDLE (GREEN)

EMERGENCY
OXYGEN HOSE

SEAT CUSHION

SURVIVAL KIT
DEPLOYMENT
HANDLE (ORANGE)

INERTIA REEL
LOCK LEVER

RESTRAINT
RELEASE HANDLE
(BLACK AND YELLOW)

THUMB LATCH

OXYGEN/COMMUNICATION
LEADS

LEG RESTRAINTS

SEAT ADJUST
SWITCH

Stencel S111S ejection seat.

sitting in the helicopter and his saturated clothing he found it very hard to move his legs. This, together with the ache in his back created a major panic as thoughts of the possibility of paralysis flooded his mind. After landing he was asked if he could walk and did not know the answer until his feet touched the deck and supported his weight — a very frightening few moments.

In looking back 20 years to the incident Lt-Cdr Eatwell sums it up:

'In retrospect the whole day was one of frustration with the pressure steadily mounting. When we eventually got airborne we only had minutes to reach the ship which was rapidly running out of sea room. The pilot was straight off the "pipeline" and under considerable pressure when we suddenly had an engine failure at a critical point in the circuit from which recovery was impossible.

'However, the strangest phenomenon of the whole incident was the dream I had the previous night. The details were not totally exact but the resulting ejection did occur. I would not say that I believe in dreams foretelling the future, but on this occasion it was certainly true.

'The one good point was that my Nav Bag had been mistakenly borrowed by another observer and was found intact in my locker, whilst the Senior Observer lost his, together with all his carefully prepared maps and charts!'

Some five months later he returned to front-line flying. His very first sortie was a continuation of the last Buccaneer flight . . . a Mk 1 aircraft which by then were few and far between, and the same pilot. This time they brought it home in one piece.

Nine years before it was incidents such as this that caused grave concern in the US Navy and, very much impressed by the success of the test ejections carried out by Sqn Ldr Fifield, it approached Martin-Baker to see if it could provide a seat with ground-level capability for some of the US Navy aircraft.

As early as 11 October 1945 two US Navy officers, Cdr J. J. Ide and Lt R. B. Barnes, had visited Denham and observed seats on the 65ft rig. After seeing competitive types the USN placed an order with the company for a 110ft rig and a complete ejection seat. This was erected under the personal supervision of James Martin and the first live shot using the rig took place in the Philadelphia Navy Yard on 15 August 1946 with Cdr D. W. Cressley taking the ride. A seat was also installed in the rear of a Douglas A-26 and on 1 November 1946, Lt Furtek USN became the first American Naval officer to carry out a live test ejection, following in the footsteps of the USAF's Sgt Lambert who had tested a seat from a P-61 the previous August.

In 1957 commercial interests in the USA were strongly against the purchase of British ejection seats and rumours denigrating the work of Martin-Baker were much in evidence. To counter these and prove that survivable ground-level ejection was possible, James Martin voiced the opinion that a live demonstration would silence the critics. This was a view shared by senior US Navy officers, and accordingly two Mk 5 seats were installed in a Grumman Cougar, then in extensive use as a Navy trainer, and on 28 August 1957, Flg Off Sidney Hughes, a young Hunter pilot from No 66 Squadron, ejected from the rear cockpit as the aircraft took off at the US Navy Airtest Center at Patuxent River, Maryland. This effectively silenced the opposition and orders from the US Navy were placed. Initially 10 different types of Navy aircraft were involved, all except the F-4 Phantom being retrospectively fitted with Martin-Baker seats replacing those of American manufacture. The front fuselages of the 10 types were delivered to Denham where the best method of modification and installation was worked out: this was a tremendous task because the seat had to be fitted without major alterations to the cockpit or canopy ejection system. As well as designing and making the seat, attachment brackets and fittings to enable ejection loads to be absorbed into the airframe also had to be designed and produced. Altogether over 20 American aircraft were eventually to be fitted with Martin-Baker seats, although when the US Marines opted to buy the Harrier (AV-8B) a campaign to replace the Martin-Baker seats with American types was successfully mounted, indicating that the battle lost in 1957 still rankled.

Following the successful demonstrations and the introduction of modifications requested primarily by the US Navy, the Mk 5 seat started to be introduced into that service between 1957 and 1960. In general it was the same pattern as the Mk 4 and included the 80ft/sec gun, 1¼sec time-delay with 'g' switch, barostatic control and duplex drogues. To meet specific US Navy crash requirements the seat structure and harness were strengthened to withstand deceleration loads of 40g instead of the 25g of the British specifications. The seat also had breaking points on the head-box to shatter the canopy and enable ejection through it. This was primarily for installation in the Grumman Cougar: on the majority of the other Mk 5 seats the American system of canopy jettison was linked with the face blind firing handle.

At this time NATO air forces also looked towards Martin-Baker for seats for their aircraft obtained under the offshore procurement programme. North American F-86 Sabre and Republic RF-84F Thunderflash aircraft of the Norwegian Air Force were the first of many NATO aircraft to be flown into Chalgrove where Mk 5 seats replaced the original American designs. It was however the Danish Air Force which was the first foreign customer. In June 1947 the British Ministry decided that Martin-Baker seats would be fitted as standard to all new jet fighters for the RAF, and in 1950 Denmark followed this lead by purchasing 20 Meteor F8s fitted with Mk 1 seats. The association continued for 36 years and ended with the retirement of the F-104 from RDAF service.

As development of ejection seats progressed it also became necessary to take a close look at other personal survival equipment. Saab and Martin-Baker were both aware of the need to do this from the earliest days, and it has already been mentioned how dinghy packs, parachutes and oxygen equipment have been developed by the companies or with their close co-operation by other specialist manufacturers. It is of course impossible to detail every single item of personal survival equipment that has been improved or originated from the experience of emergency escapes. However, one such piece of equipment is the Personal Equipment Connecter (PEC), whose rationale is to reduce the number of attachments that a crew member has to his aircraft, thus increasing his chances of escape if faced with a problem that requires instant reaction.

The PEC designed by Martin-Baker has turned what was a complex operation of 'strapping in' into a single action. The unit consists of three elements: the seat portion, the parts connected to the occupant, and those connected to the aircraft.

The first is permanently attached to the seat pan, and the other two are detachable from it and connected respectively to the occupant's equipment, and a static line to the aircraft. When the seat is activated, the supplies of anti-g, oxygen and air ventilation as well as the tel/mic are automatically disconnected and sealed, whilst the emergency oxygen is switched on and admitted to the mask via the main oxygen supply line. On ejection the static line pulls away the aircraft portion, and on separation from the seat the occupant's component is released, the air ventilating suit supply line being provided with a valve to prevent ingress of water in the event of a descent into the sea. An important feature is that coupling of all services is simultaneous and can easily be checked by use of the tel/mic, which, if speech is audible, shows that oxygen and the other supplies are correctly connected. Such items as the PEC became vital components of aircrew equipment and it is now hard to envisage just how ejectees managed before its introduction.

But in some cases investigation into crew survival equipment have not had a warm reception, and others have been rejected for reasons that were hard to understand. One such piece of equipment was the rear-facing ejection seat designed for the three crew members accommodated behind the two pilots in British V-bombers, the Valiant, Victor and Vulcan. The design of the aircraft was such that the pilot and co-pilot were equipped with Martin-Baker seats, whereas the Air Electronics Officer (AEO) and two navigators, who sat behind the other two at a slightly lower level and facing the aircraft's tail, had in the event of an emergency to leave the aircraft through a door fitted with a blast screen (Valiant and Victor) or a downwards swinging hatch (Vulcan).

There was a lot of controversy relating to the moral aspect of whether or not pilots would eject and leave the crew to their own fate. In many cases the fact that there was a laid-down emergency procedure — which if operated efficiently enabled the three rear members to leave exceptionally quickly and have their parachutes opened by static lines — was overlooked. The question of sufficient height often came into the picture and early discussions tended to ignore the fact that when the aircraft were designed the available seats did not have low-level capability anyway, so this argument was something of a red herring. Generalisation can be very dangerous, but when asked their views many V-bomber crew members were not too worried and felt that they would have had a good chance of getting out from the rear positions providing they all followed the much practised drills. What probably brought the matter to the attention of the public (via the popular media, who for a time mounted a relentless campaign for ejection seats for all V-bomber crew members, and then equally quickly dropped it) was the unfortunate accident to the RAF's first Vulcan, XA897, at London's Heathrow Airport on 1 October 1956. The aircraft was returning from a very successful flag-waving world tour and in poor weather undershot on the approach. Sqn Ldr Donald Howard, the Vulcan's pilot and captain, and his co-pilot, AM Sir Harry Broadhurst, ejected when it became clear that the delta-winged bomber was beyond control, but the three other crew members and a civilian technician from Avro were all killed. The seats installed in this aircraft were among the first Mk 3s with low-level capability.

The press made much of the incident, especially the absence of ejection seats in the back of the aircraft, and this and the fact that all crew members of the American B-47 had ejection seats, was instrumental in Martin-Baker looking at the feasibility of producing rearwards-facing seats and operating them successfully in a sequential system (to prevent collision).

A specially designed seat was installed in a Valiant and after a series of static tests a programme of three dummy ejections, one from the runway during take-off and two at 250kt and 300kt at 200ft, were planned. These commenced on 27 June 1960, the runway test taking place when the aircraft reached 100kt. This was totally satisfactory, the parachute being fully deployed 4.3sec after ejection initiation and allowing for a fully controlled drop of 38ft. The tests were rounded off on 1 July 1960 over Chalgrove when W. T. 'Doddy' Hay ejected from the Valiant which had taken-off from RAF Finningley, at a height of 1,000ft and an IAS of 250kt. (A graphic account of this test and others in which Mr Hay was involved is contained in his book, *The Man in the Hot Seat* originally published by Collins Ltd in London.)

The ejection, watched by several senior RAF officers as well as officials from the Ministry of Aviation and HQ Bomber Command, was a great success and proved without any doubt that ejection from V-bombers using a rearwards-facing seat presented no problems. Incidentally, it is believed that this was the first rearward-facing live ejection in the world.

The cost of this experimental work was close to £¼ million and hopes were high that a decision would be taken to retrospectively fit seats to all V-bombers. However it was not to be, and eventually the Ministry of Defence announced it had decided against such a move. For a short while there were banner headlines in the newspapers which had been foremost in mounting the campaign for seats for rear crew members, and questions were asked in the House, but the decision was not reversed. It can only be presumed that it was influenced by many factors including total costs, which are outside the scope of this narrative.

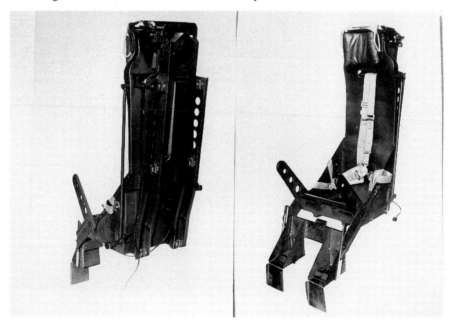

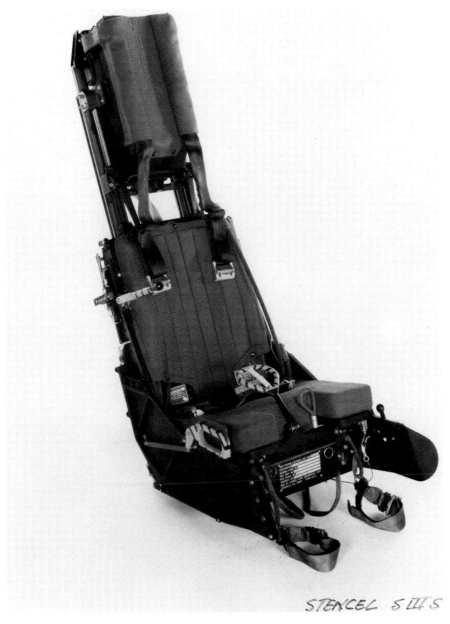

STENCEL S III S

Above:
A Stencel seat as used in the AV-8B Harrier. Note the firing handles and leg restraints.
Bryan Wilburn

Left:
Front and rear views of the short-lived ML Aviation seat. *Graham Carter*

85

Above:
A test shot of the proposed rearward-facing seat for use on Britain's V-bombers. This occasion was the ejection of a dummy from a Valiant on 27 June 1960. *Martin-Baker*

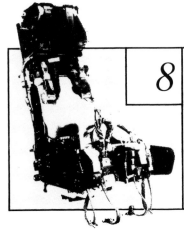

8 Continuing The Line

In a paper presented to the Royal Aeronautical Society in 1966, Sir James Martin, as he was by then, commented: 'Although, due to intensive development work over the years, the seat was greatly improved in performance, I was still disturbed by the fact that the fatality rate during ejections in our seats was still about 12% and this meant that 20 or so pilots were being killed every year in ejections. Well over half these were due entirely to lack of altitude at the time of ejection. It was therefore plain that if the trajectory height could be increased on ejection, we should save many more lives. As the limit had already been reached with ejection guns, only a rocket propulsion system would give a trajectory height enough to be worthwhile.'

Analysis of fatal accidents indicated that 60% occurred at low altitude with the aircraft descending at a high sink rate, and in most cases the ejection sequence was developing satisfactorily but the pilot struck the ground with the parachute streaming but not developing. This, at a time when successful recovery with the standard cartridge-fired gun had reached a figure of around 93%, might well have prompted lesser men to have adopted a reluctant but understandable philosophy of acceptance. But not Sir James Martin. To him every young life lost was almost a personal blow, and his determination to reduce further the failure figure led to the above comment, made some five years after research into rocket-powered seats had started.

Before looking at the solution, the story of Flt Lt Ken Topaz, who is believed to be the first Air Electronics Officer (AEO) to save his life using an ejection seat, is notable, for it proves that to every rule there is an exception.

On 3 May 1966, Flt Lt Topaz was the Air Electronics Officer of an Electronic Counter Measures (ECM) Canberra B2, WH857, briefed to carry out an exercise in the Yeovilton area. The aircraft, carrying a full fuel load including tip tanks, taxied to the end of the runway at RAF Watton, Norfolk, as the three crew members busied themselves with pre-take-off checks. It was a typical English spring day, the deep blue of the sky being enhanced by the yellow ball of the sun which had chased off all the early morning clouds. There was a slight cross-wind, but nothing serious enough to cause the very experienced pilot any concern as he called for take-off clearance and swung the Canberra on to the centre-line of the runway. At precisely 10.20hrs the aircraft was airborne, and as the Norfolk countryside slipped below, the crew reported that all systems were serviceable. The navigator, a Canadian officer on exchange posting, passed the first heading to the pilot, then settled back to savour what was scheduled to be his last Canberra sortie before he returned to Canada.

As the aircraft left Watton, part of the electronic equipment became unserviceable, and despite the efforts of the Air Electronics Officer, remained so. Without this piece of equipment it was impossible to carry on with the briefed sortie, so the pilot abandoned it and advised Watton air traffic that he was returning. Rather than make the whole trip abortive, the captain decided that he would get some value from it by carrying out a *Gee* homing and let-down, leading into an ACR 7 pickup.

As the Canberra approached the pick-up point, the captain reduced power on the starboard engine to an idle position — a state where the power unit gave zero thrust and no drag — the objective being to carry out an asymmetric approach and landing. Contact with radar was established at five miles, and an approach to the runway was started. As the pilot and navigator exchanged the litany of normal pre-landing checks, the Air Electronics Officer started to shut down his equipment and tighten his seat harness, a procedure he always adopted once the aircraft was on finals.

The radar talk-down continued until at one mile the controller reported: 'You are one mile from touch-down, look ahead and land visually.' At this point the Air Electronics Officer looked forward into the cockpit and quite clearly saw the reflection of the lead-in lights on the inside of the canopy. Although he considered this unusual, he had not at that time flown many hours in Canberras and was prepared to accept it as normal. Almost at the same time, the navigator who was sitting alongside to his left, pointed to the ASI which was falling through 85kt, and the altimeter which was reading below 100ft.

At the weight the Canberra was flying, the speed across the hedge should have been about 125kt, so it was very slow at this point of the approach. The two rear crew members said nothing, but suddenly noticed that full power was being applied to both engines. The port 'live' one picked up immediately, but the idling one seemed to catch then surge, and probably flamed out. The aircraft started to yaw sharply and rolled to starboard, the port wing came up to the almost vertical position, then the Canberra flick-rolled very rapidly to port and the wing tank hit the perimeter track just to the left of the runway. The Canberra cartwheeled about the port wing, eventually striking its nose on the ground and breaking off this section just forward of the main spar, coming to rest about 500yd from the point of first impact. It is perhaps not too surprising that the Air Electronics Officer has no memory of his actual ejection from the aircraft: in fact he can only recall the wingtip striking the ground and then finding himself sitting on his parachute pack on the airfield.

In the B2 the rear seats were arranged side by side with the guide rails angled slightly away from each other to give crew separation. As both men left the aircraft, the navigator's seat hit the frangible hatch first — the explosive bolts removing this had not been fired — and it attached itself to the top of his seat. The added weight and drag of the hatch prevented the navigator's seat from attaining any height, and he hit the ground with a high forward speed which caused serious injuries from which he died soon after. The angle of the guide rails and slightly delayed ejection of the AEO, coupled to the fact that as he was on the starboard side of the aircraft he was fired away from the angle of crash, gave him enough height to have a chance. The barostat on the seat ran down very quickly, as would be expected at this low level, and separation took place at zero forward speed, with the occupant in a normal sitting position. So in effect he was deposited on his feet, almost as though he had simply stepped from the aircraft. The timing of the ejection, and the angle the seat made with the horizontal, were by good fortune absolutely correct. It is doubtful if such a situation could ever be simulated.

Sadly both other crew members were killed, but apart from a small scratch on his left ankle, Flt Lt Topaz suffered no injuries. He went on to join the V-force and left the RAF in 1974.

The parameters of the Martin-Baker 1CN seat used by Flt Lt Topaz were minima of 1,000ft and 125kt. As far as it is possible to ascertain he left the Canberra below 80kt and certainly well under 100ft, so it is not too surprising that at a subsequent dinner given by Martin-Baker to ejectees, Sir James said to him, 'I did not design *that* seat to do what you did with it my boy.'

But the rocket-powered seat he designed did give many other aircrew in similar situations the chance of survival without the intervention of Lady Luck. As already mentioned the prime aim was a higher trajectory without any increase in physiological forces. At first it looked as though the rocket charge could be housed within the ejection gun itself, but to get a nozzle of sufficient size and correct shape to ensure a constant thrust line proved impossible in the limited space available. The design therefore consisted of a pair of steel combustion tubes mounted to the rear of the seat pan and joined to an efflux chamber which discharged downwards below the seat. Tests culminated with a live ejection on 1 April 1961 by 'Doddy' Hay under zero speed and altitude conditions. This was a total success with Hay achieving a descent of 200ft on a fully deployed parachute. At the Paris Air Show later that year, Hay carried out a most impressive repeat before the public, who were astonished by the seat's peformance. Although tests with this rocket motor were totally successful, the system used was abandoned in favour of a multi-tube rocket pack which could be fitted beneath the seat pan, with the thrust line almost vertical and passing through the centre of gravity of the ejected mass.

The pack was attached to the pan in a manner which facilitated quick and simple removal and replacement without the need of special tools, which greatly simplified the retrospective fitting of the rocket system to seats already in service. The rocket pack consists of a number of combustion tubes, containing a solid propellant, which are screwed into a central gallery mounted across the bottom of the seat pan. This gallery also houses the efflux nozzles screwed into its underside and pointing downwards. The number of nozzles varies according to the design characteristics of the seat/rocket combination and is usually between two, on the Mk 7DQ seat, and six, on the Mk 9. One of the combustion tubes is fitted with a mechanical firing mechanism and cartridge. As the seat nears the end of the ejection gun stroke, a static line attached to the floor of the cockpit withdraws the sear from the firing mechanism allowing the spring-loaded firing pin to descend and fire the cartridge. This produces a very hot flame which flashes through the tube causing simultaneous ignition. To guarantee correct light-up characteristics, the efflux nozzles are sealed by metal discs which blow out when the correct pressure build-up has been reached. The standard rocket pack was fitted with combustion tubes of approximately 1in diameter and gave safe ejection under

Above:
Sir James Martin with W. T. 'Doddy' Hay after the successful first test of a rocket seat on 1 April 1961. *Martin-Baker*

Below:
The 1in rocket pack fitted to the Mk DQ7 seat. *Martin-Baker*

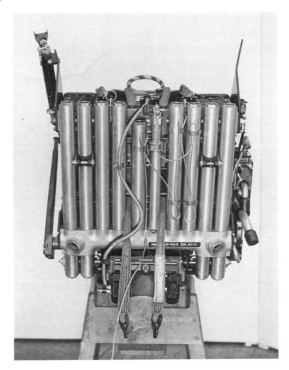

Mk 9 Martin-Baker gas-operated seat firing system.

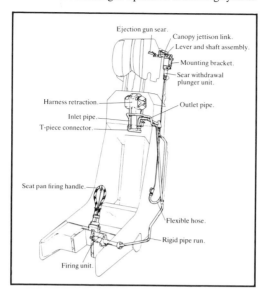

Ejection gun sear.

Canopy jettison link.

Lever and shaft assembly.

Mounting bracket.

Sear withdrawal
plunger unit.

Harness retraction.

Outlet pipe.

Inlet pipe.

T-piece connector.

Seat pan firing handle.

Flexible hose.

Rigid pipe run.

Firing unit.

Below:
The Martin-Baker inclined rig for testing rocket seats.   *Martin-Baker*

conditions of zero altitude and with a sink rate of up to 30ft/sec. However, VTOL aircraft such as the Harrier can encounter extremely high sink rates should an emergency occur whilst they are in the hover mode, and it was for this reason that a pack using 2in diameter tubes was developed. This motor is larger and designed to give the seat a trajectory high enough to ensure escape from an aircraft with a sink rate approaching 80ft/sec.

Early tests were carried out on ground test rigs and, for slow-speed trials, an adapted motor vehicle. When these proved satisfactory a Meteor 7 for medium-speed and a Hunter T7 for high-speed air tests were employed. Once again when all tests proved that the system worked, it was necessary to make a live ejection. On 13 March 1962, Wg Cdr Peter Howard, an RAF doctor from the Institute of Aviation Medicine and a specialist in Aviation Physiology, ejected himself from a Meteor at a speed of 250kt and an altitude of 250ft. After landing he commented favourably on the smooth ride which was mainly due to a significant reduction in acceleration, the peak 'g' being about 15, and the rise about 160g/sec.

To evaluate the rocket seat when ejection took place at speed close to the ground, with the aircraft in a nose-down attitude, Martin-Baker constructed a 200ft long rig with one end supported on a tower 80ft high, and the other on the ground, giving an inclination of 20°. The seat under test is fitted to a rocket sled, which is hauled to the top and then propelled at speed down the incline, ejection being initiated at a predetermined point. In addition to this a 6,000ft long 'supersonic' sled track is also used to test seats at very high speed. This track is in itself an engineering masterpiece which is straight within a tolerance of 00.010in over 125ft, such accuracy being essential to minimise horizontal and vertical loads when travelling at high speed. The sled accommodates replica fuselages and test cockpits of the aircraft in which the seat under test is to be fitted.

The cockpit is fully representative of the subject aircraft and its sub-systems such as canopy jettison and interseat sequencing systems; a fully clothed and equipped dummy is also installed. Speed is varied by the number of motors fitted to the sled and up to 15 can be used. Such an installation develops a combined thrust of 112,800lb for 2.25sec and accelerates the vehicle to over 600kt. The high-speed test facility is UK, US and NATO approved and has been used to test the escape systems of the Tornado, Mirage, EA-6B Prowler, Maachi 339, CASA 101, IAI Kfir, and the Saab JAS39 Gripen, to mention just a few.

In addition to the tests briefly mentioned, a large programme of evaluation of the Martin-Baker seat has been carried out in the USA with special reference to the installation in the Intruder, Crusader and F-4 Phantom. Many of the tests were carried out under the direction of the Bureau of Naval Weapons at its laboratories at Dahlgran, Philadelphia, and on the high-speed sled track at China Lake. As long ago as September 1965 the US Navy decided to fit the rocket seat into the aircraft mentioned as well as other types.

A refinement fitted to later rocket seats, to compensate for a variance in weight of occupants, was the provision of a control for adjusting the angle of thrust of the rocket in relation to the seat. Known as the 'pitch control unit' it is mounted on the side of the seat pan and comprises a handwheel attached to a vertical screwjack, the lower end of which is connected to the forward part of the rocket pack. Turning the handwheel causes the front of the rocket to rise or fall thus varying the angle of the rocket's thrust and ensuring that it will pass through the centre of gravity of the ejected mass. A scale calibrated in pounds or kilogrammes moves in a glazed aperture as adjustments are made by the occupant as he enters his 'dressed weight'.

Introduction of the rocket pack to the range of Mk 4 and Mk 5 seats created the basic Mks 6 and 7 respectively. However, many of the latter were subsequently modified with additional improvements in design such as power retraction systems, remotely-fired rocket and sequencing systems. Briefly, the first mentioned ensured that the ejectee was automatically pulled back into the correct posture for ejection. This was accomplished by two straps attached to the shoulder harness, each being wound around a reel. The two reels are mounted on a horizontal shaft rotated under power provided by a cartridge linked to the firing mechanism. Delays are incorporated to ensure that ejection does not commence before retraction is complete. The power retraction units allow total freedom of movement for the occupant during normal flight manoeuvres, the straps pulling out as he moves forward and retracting on their reels as he moves back. If a high 'g' force is encountered the reels automatically lock preventing further forward movement until the force is removed; this is in much the same manner as modern inertia reel safety belts fitted to cars operate.

The remote rocket firing system was introduced to overcome the problem of vulnerability with the static line firing system. The revised method consisted of a firing unit mounted high on the seat containing a sear-operated firing pin and cartridge, with the static line coiled inside the unit out of danger from accidental damage. One end is attached to the sear and the other to the aircraft, usually one of the trip rods for the drogue gun or the TRU. As the seat leaves the aircraft, the sear is withdrawn, pulls taut and removes the sear to fire the cartridge. Gas pressure produced is directed through a rigid pipe and flexible hose to a gas-operated firing unit in the rocket, which fires the rocket propellant.

The Mk 8 seat was developed for the ill-fated TSR2 and, although it was never produced in quantity, provided a great deal of valuable information for the later Mk 9 and Mk 10 designs.

The Mk 9 introduced major changes including the power retraction system described, a new gas-operated seat firing system, and parachute and seat pan design changes. The cable system employed on earlier seats and the interim method used on the Mk 7 were completely replaced by the gas-operated method which was activated by the seat pan handle, now the only one fitted, the long-standing overhead face screen handle disappearing completely. When the seat handle is pulled, the firing handle sear, in a breech unit beneath it, is removed and a cartridge is fired. The gas released does two things: it is piped to and operates the harness retraction unit, as well as going to the sear withdrawal unit where a rotating cross-shaft at the top of the seat withdraws a sear from the ejection gun and allows the firing pin to hit the gun's cartridge and start the ejection sequence. On this seat the parachute is stowed in a container in the back of the seat pan while the drogue parachutes are housed behind the occupant's head at the top of the seat. The front of the drogue container is upholstered and contoured to accommodate the pilot's protective helmet (bone dome) and provides some head restraint. The parachute withdrawal line runs in a vertical channel in the middle of the headrest, and the top of the parachute is covered by flaps secured by rip pins withdrawn by a line attached to the drogue shackle.

The introduction of a torso harness, which was put on in the crew room before strapping into the aircraft's seat, was another advance in crew equipment and was first used by the RAF in the Phantom. The original design did have its shortcomings which included little negative 'g' restraint, so the UK version adopted for the Harrier, Jaguar and Buccaneer was improved to provide this. This was but the first step of many changes as even the improved version initially suffered from a lack of single-point release.

Problems with the fasteners, the need to provide one harness per man rather than per seat, the extra weight and heat load outside the cockpit, an increased rate of wear whilst the crew were on standby, the need for expert fitting and a short operational life made the torso harness relatively expensive. To overcome all the disadvantages a new type of seat-mounted combined harness similar to that used in the Jet Provost was developed for the Hawk and Tornado. Known as the Simplified Combined Harness (SCH), it produces levels of restraint equal to the torso harness but without the attendant disadvantages. The SCH was retrofitted to the Phantom, Harrier, Jaguar and Buccaneer. It is fitted to the Mk 10 seat and as its name implies is a combined parachute/seat harness. It has a quick-release fitting permanently on the negative-'g' strap, the lower end of which is held in a lock in the seat pan. The rest of the harness consists of two lap straps, two leg loops, two shoulder straps and a back pad attached to the straps. Legs fitted to the lower end of each shoulder strap are the only two connections made into the quick-release box when strapping in. Each leg loop is passed through a 'D' ring on the extremity of the relevant lap strap and the appropriate shoulder strap is passed through the leg loop before plugging into the quick-release.

The upper end of each shoulder strap is provided with a roller shackle, through which are passed the straps of the harness power retraction unit, which are then plugged into the top of the harness locks. The lower straps are equipped with two metal lugs which plug into the lower harness locks. Although this sounds complicated it is in fact quite simple and considerably quickens and simplifies strapping-in procedures, as well as providing a marked improvement in comfort and an increase in the degree of restraint. During research the author was fitted into a Mk 10 seat at Boscombe Down, and although initially one feels a little like a trussed-up chicken, once everything is in place the freedom of movement and comfort is hard to believe. This is especially apparent when the firing handle is operated and the sequence starts with the operation of the power retraction unit pulling one firmly back into the seat.

Another improvement with the Mk 10 is a new manual separation system catering for the unlikely failure of the barostat and drogue gun either above or below the height set on the TRU. One pull on the manual separation override handle initiates a totally automatic sequence culminating with the deployment of the personal parachute, without the occupant having to deploy this with a separate action of the ripcord. A safety lock interconnected with the seat firing handle prevents the manual separation handle from being activated unless the seat firing handle is first withdrawn.

Safety locks and pins have been a feature of all seats, and the multiplicity of them and their stowage was a drill that had to be remembered and carried out implicitly. These are now replaced by one pin which makes the seat totally safe when the aircraft is parked.

Following on from the breakthrough represented by the gas-operated seat firing system of the Mk 9, the Mk 10 seat embodied the following design changes:

1. Extension of the gas-operated firing system introduced on the Mk 9 to include the release of the drogue, and to operate the harness release system.
2. Redesign of the barostatic TRU and drogue gun for inclusion in the gas-operated system.
3. The combination of the drogue and parachute as a complete assembly stowed in one quickly detachable container at the top of the seat structure. (This means that the parachute is now as close as it is likely to be to the point where it serves most use, above the pilot. So from the original traditional position in the seat pan forming a cushion, it has moved a small distance that could make a lot of difference as far as survival is concerned.)
4. A simplified two-point combined harness.
5. Improved design of harness power retraction.
6. Introduction of arm restraints.

The parachute now used is a GQ Aeroconical type which opens rapidly without excessive deceleration loads, enabling the time delay to be significantly shortened. The barostat time release now incorporates a 'g' controller which controls the opening of the parachute at altitudes above 6,000ft where the time to achieve full deployment is not as critical as it is at low level. This helps minimise shock loads transmitted to the occupant. An arm restraint system integrated into the pilot's clothing and seat, connected by a plug-in fitting on the upper sleeve and equipped with automatic disconnect for emergency ground egress, is another option which eliminates arm flailing.

These and other improvements as well as an overall weight reduction have introduced a capability for safe escape at zero altitude and zero speed, as well as speeds up to 630kt IAS. The Mk 10 seat has been fitted to 28 different aircraft around the world and has satisfactorily completed over 400 tests. A low-weight reduced-cost version known as the Mk 10L was developed for the Northrop F-5 and is now standard equipment in the Saab JAS39, BAe EAP, Embraer Tucano and BAe Hawk 200. It will be recalled that in the early days of the ejection seat the time from the moment of initiation of the seat to the pilot being under a deployed parachute was in the order of 6sec. With the Mk 10 seat this is now 2.95sec.

The first emergency use of a Mk 10B seat came in very dramatic circumstances when a member of the famous Red Arrows aerobatic team ejected during a low-level flypast at Brighton. 'Red Seven' hit the mast of a moored yacht and the pilot ejected at about 300ft and 250kt with 150° of starboard bank. The minimum height of a successful ejection at 250kt with that amount of bank and no rate of descent ('Red Seven' was trying to climb away after the collision) is assessed as 260ft.

The pilot's quick decision to eject came just in time and on the very edge of the survivable parameters. The margin can be very small indeed but as seat development continues the overall chances of survival increase. The command

Above:
The Martin-Baker sled track for testing rocket seats ready for action. *Martin-Baker*

Below:
The BAe Hawk 200 and EAP are among the latest aircraft equipped with the Mk 10L seat.
Martin-Baker

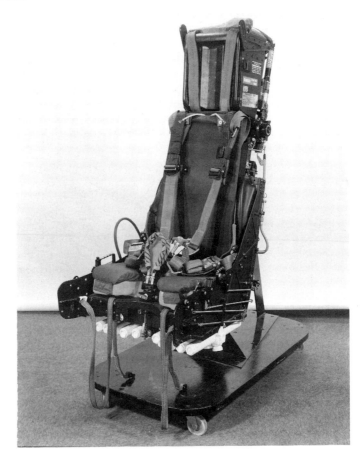

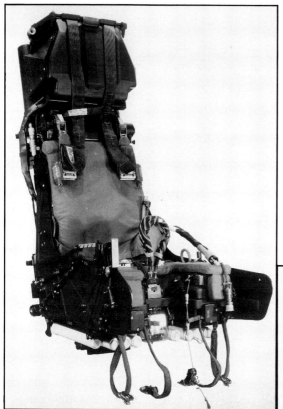

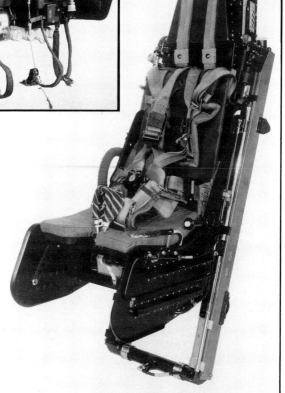

Below:
The new Pilatus PC-7 is
equipped with the Martin-Baker
Mk 15A seat which makes an
interesting comparison with
examples of the very early seats
from this company.
Martin-Baker

Above:
The world's first
microprocessor-controlled
electronic ejection seat, the
Martin-Baker Mk 14 NACES
escape system. This is the
standard seat for the F-18,
F-14D, A-6F and T-45.
Martin-Baker

97

ejection facility introduced on the Mk 10 is another example of saving precious time. Before its introduction it had been standard practice for the pilot to order his crew to eject, then follow them. At low level even this small delay could be fatal, so the command system was devised. In this the only action necessary is for the pilot to pull his own firing handle. This action results in the other crew member being ejected in a predetermined sequence which is automatic and can be selected as either operative or non-operative. The time-delay breech unit ensures that the time interval occurs between the seats ejecting before the unit fires its own cartridge to eject the other seat. Disconnect blocks are automatically disconnected by static cables as each seat leaves the aircraft.

The Mk 11 seat is based on the successful lightweight model used in the T-27 Tucano and is designed for medium performance propeller-driven training aircraft. Dispensing with the rocket pack, the seat has a ground level 60-400kt capability, and has all the features of the Mk 8L seat but with further reduced weight. The GQ Aeroconical parachute has only one stabilising drogue and the seat has a single-point harness with power retraction. A three-tube telescopic gun (one primary and two auxiliary cartridges) gives the man/seat mass a velocity of 65ft/sec in 0.2sec with a peak of 12g and a jolt of 200g/sec.

The Mk 12 seat is very similar to the Mk 10 but additionally can sense airspeed and thereby adjust the timing of parachute deployment, which in a high-speed escape prevents damage to the canopy and dangerous decelerative shock. This is achieved by a triple system of seat speed measurement and seat functions in one of three modes: low speed/low level, high speed/low level, and any speed/high level. On ejection and when clear of debris from the aircraft canopy, two pitot heads, which are normally stowed flush with the sides of the headrest, are mechanically deployed into the airstream and locked in position. One sensor is pitot/mechanical in operation, and the other pitot/electrical. The third element of this triple alliance is a heavy metal 'g' switch. If the airspeed falls below 250kt, the mode selector unit decides whether the aircraft is above or below 7,000ft. If above, high speed mode is selected; if below, low speed/low level is chosen. If the airspeed is above 250kt, high-speed mode selection will be made. In the low-speed mode, operation of the system has been so refined that the ejectee should be suspended on a fully deployed parachute in only 1.9sec after pulling the firing handle. Even in the delayed sequence of the high-speed mode, the time is only 2.45sec which is still faster than the Mk 10 seat. Divergence of the paths of ejection for multiple-seat aircraft is provided by a Lateral Thrust Motor (LTM) attached to the seat. As the main rocket ignites, the LTM also fires, but only for 0.05sec of the rocket's 0.25sec firing time. This tips the seat slightly and assures a safe divergent trajectory. And progress in overall design has not been confined to the function of the seat; in the beginning servicing and maintenance was a lengthy process, but with the Mk 12 seat a Daily Inspection (DI) takes 1min and there is a three-year servicing cycle.

In May 1985 Martin-Baker was awarded a contract by the United States Navy to produce and develop a new high-technology escape system, designated the Navy Aircrew Common Ejection Seat (NACES), for installation in the F/A-18 Hornet, T-45 Hawk and Grumman F-14 Tomcat. The new seat employs an on-seat sensory system and microprocessor-controlled electronic sequencer to enable it to respond to the flight conditions at the time of ejection and to control the operation of the seat to achieve maximum aircrew recovery. This Mk 14 seat, which at the time of writing is still in the test stage, will incorporate the very latest technology and engineering and will undoubtedly form the stepping stone to a seat of the future that will think and act for itself, and eject the crew when it knows that ejection is the only answer, whatever recovery action they may attempt.

It is clearly impossible to cover every single aspect of ejection seat design and development in the space available, but before taking a more detailed look at some examples of how ejection seats have saved lives it is worth briefly touching on an interesting development that was not uppermost in the designers' minds when the seat was first conceived — underwater ejection.

Superstition may or may not have played a part in the decision to omit 13 from the sequence of seat designations, but it may be significant that a number of very interesting incidents have occurred on the 13th of the month. These include the first ever underwater ejection, which took place from Wyvern TF1 VZ783 'X' of No 813 Squadron on 13 October 1954. A Martin-Baker 11B seat ejected pilot Lt Bruce Macfarlane RN, whose report covers every aspect of the incident, and is reproduced almost verbatim:

'I was sitting with the seat not fully lowered but in a medium-to-up position. The cockpit canopy was tight shut. Oxygen mask was on and I was taking normal flow oxygen, and had been since starting the engine 10min previously. The emergency oxygen tube was not connected. R/T lead was plugged in. Air pipe from ventilated suit was connected to supply. Dinghy pack was not connected at side tabs, but lanyard was fastened to Mae West (life jacket), up through the legs. Parachute harness was done up but box was in quick release position. (Fastening and unfastening parachute straps whilst flying has been found to be most awkward.)

'Seat harness was pulled tight and secure. Goggles were not worn, but were pushed up on crash helmet [sic].

'In this condition I was catapulted from the deck of HMS *Albion*; the engine failed at the beginning of the run and the aircraft dived at about 20° or 30° from the ship's bows into the sea.

'Catapulting is a somewhat startling experience and I personally am just about off the bows before I collect my wits enough to be aware of anything and take control of the aircraft.

'In this case my first realisation was loss of power: I tried to open the throttle but this was already locked in the open position. The next instant I hit the sea — I suppose at about 70kt, wheels down and flaps in the take-off position.

'I knew that Wyvern aircraft have extremely bad ditching characteristics and I had in fact witnessed a fatal ditching some 18 months ago when the aircraft entered the sea and disappeared immediately without any hesitation at all before sinking.

'This memory flashed through my mind just before I hit the sea and I felt then that I had no chance of escape. The impact with the water stunned me to some extent.

'By the time I had collected my wits again I was underwater and it was getting darker. I had one thought. To get out of the aircraft. My nervous state at this time seemed to disconnect my body from my brain — except for my left hand.

'The yellow emergency canopy jettison knob filled my whole vision. I was grateful for its colour and position. I hit it with my left hand and the canopy unlocked, and green water started to pour in all round the edges. I did not notice the canopy actually go and it may have been still more or less in position when I ejected. I pulled the blind handle with my left hand only, immediately after hitting the hood jettison lever.

'Tears on the right side of my Mae West and a tear on the left sleeve of my flying overall (which penetrated through to a 3in scratch on my left forearm) could have been caused by ejection up through the canopy. I was wearing a crash helmet and the actual ejection seemed identical to that on the test rig.

'I pulled the firing handle, nothing happened (as on the test rig) and I knew that I had to pull it a little further. I was fired out, and blacked out momentarily, the next awareness being that I was out of the aircraft. I have no way of knowing, but I imagine that I ejected at about 10ft to 20ft below the surface with the aircraft in about a 30° nosedown position. In any case, ejection did not bring me to the surface. When I ejected I did nothing with my legs. I did not bring my feet back towards the seat. I did not lose my shoes or suffer any leg injuries. In fact after the aircraft entered the sea the bows of the ship hit it and cut the rear fuselage in two; the tail and a collapsed fuselage fuel tank were seen from the helicopter to pass down the starboard side of the ship. I myself finally surfaced astern to port, about 200yd behind the ship. I assume I was out before the ship hit the aircraft. I was not aware of any impact shock.

'As soon as I collected my wits again after ejection, I was aware of being tumbled violently over and over in light green sea, becoming tangled in the seat. I saw yellow nylon by my face, supposedly the drogue chute. I had choked in quite a lot of sea water by this time and that drowning aspect was no longer unpleasant, very like drinking fresh water.

'During this head-over-heels tumbling in the ship's wake or possibly under the ship, I must have undone my parachute straps, though I have no clear memory of this. Probably at this time too I lost my crash helmet, inner flying helmet, and perhaps oxygen mask. Anyway when I finally surfaced I did not have these items.

'Eventually the tumbling stopped and I thought I was going to live and then, with the most bitter disappointment, I began to be dragged slowly down, deeper and deeper. I must have reached an advanced stage of drowning. I was in a dreamy, relaxed, comfortable but sad state, slowly "floating" deeper. I had given up the struggle. Suddenly all the tangle freed itself, a spark of life reached my brain — the dinghy lanyard was still pulling down. I followed my hand down and fumbled twice with the release catch and undid it. Then I began rising. For the first time I now had a very desperate need for air: I tried to swim upwards. I suddenly remembered my Mae West, and to help me reach the surface as quickly as possible I inflated it, and popped upwards like a cork into the sunshine. The helicopter with strop lowered seemed almost right there waiting for me and I was soon picked up and back on board the carrier.'

In analysing his amazing escape Lt Macfarlane concluded that he should perhaps have inflated his life jacket earlier, which may well have brought him to the surface despite the entangled debris and his dinghy pack. He also felt that the helmet had given very good protection to his head and face during the ejection, and that experience on the test rig had been time well spent. Like all good aircrew he had always spent time practising escape drills: one of these had been pretending to hit the hood jettison lever and then eject, every time he entered the Wyvern's cockpit. This became second nature and certainly paid dividends.

The escape was of course of tremendous interest to Martin-Baker and the firm started to take a careful look into every aspect of underwater ejection. This presented many new problems and challenges, not the least of which were the increasing water pressure as the aircraft sank, and the not inconsiderable one of the seat's automatic function releasing the drogue and parachute — naturally not of prime importance for survival in such situations.

From that fateful day an underwater system was developed, and it provides automatic escape from submerged aircraft even though the occupants may be unconscious. An ejection seat fitted with this system is capable of ejecting the occupant from the aircraft, separating him from the seat, and bringing him to the surface by means of a fully inflated life jacket, without any action on his part.

Incorporation of the equipment provides the standard seat with the underwater escape facility, but in no way affects the normal ballistic operation during an airborne ejection. Modifications consists of an air cylinder mounted either on the seat or the aircraft bulkhead and charged to 3,000lb/sq in. Air from the cylinder is released at a predetermined depth, and pressure is directed into the ejection gun cylinder. This results in the extension of the ejection gun tubes and subsequent seat ejection. Air is also piped to a drogue gun trip rod release unit to disconnect the trip rod and prevent the gun from firing and deploying the drogues.

The TRU operates as in a normal ejection to give seat/man separation. Bladders positioned behind the parachute pack inflate during separation to push the occupant clear of the seat. Parachute deployment is prevented by cutting the withdrawal line by a guillotine as the occupant leaves the seat.

After separation, the ejectee rises to the surface aided by his life jacket which is inflated by pressure from a CO_2 cylinder mounted on the jacket and actuated by air pressure from the air cylinder.

From below the sea to ground level and the stratosphere, the ejection seat is now a vital piece of safety equipment and accepted without question. The next challenge facing designers is a system for use in space, which will clearly involve some form of capsule with its own life support system. Early designs already exist, and no doubt in 60 years or so these will make the present series of high technology seats appear as primitive as some of the early aeroplanes now look to those of us who have grown up in the jet age.

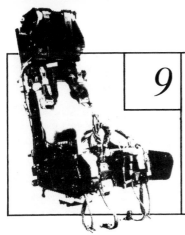

9 Part Two Ejection To Captivity

In the immediate postwar years RAF Fighter Command was equipped with early marks of Vampires and Meteors which had been on the drawing board during the development period of the ejection seat and were not fitted with it. Pilots therefore had to trust the old-fashioned and risky method of escape, by diving over the side or inverting their aircraft and dropping out, neither of which gave much hope at high Mach numbers or 'g' levels. The Meteor F8 was the first of the Gloster fighters to be fitted with the Martin-Baker seat, and this must have added a lot to pilots' peace of mind, especially after Jo Lancaster had shown that escape in an emergency was possible. Ironically, it was a Royal Navy pilot who was to be the first British serviceman to owe his life to the ejection seat.

On 20 March 1951, Lt P. L. McDermot RN suffered an engine failure in a Vickers Supermarine Attacker of the Royal Navy Air Fighting Development Unit of the CFE based at RAF West Raynham in Norfolk. The damage to the engine was such that Lt McDermot had no chance of recovery so at a height of 7,500ft and an airspeed of 230kt he abandoned the aircraft. The ejection went off without a hitch and he landed uninjured, having added one small niche of fame to the Attacker's rather undistinguished career.

It is of interest that the aircraft recorded this first whilst operating from the Central Fighter Establishment at West Raynham as this was the station that was to hit the headlines of the national dailies in February 1956 when six Hunters from the Day Fighter Leaders' School were involved in the largest multiple ejection on the same day on record. Although there has always been friendly rivalry between the Fleet Air Arm and the RAF, Lt McDermot's ejection was probably an event that the RAF were happy to concede to the Senior Service. However, it was inevitable that the RAF's turn would come, and sure enough this occurred in a double dose in July 1951. On 3 July, Sgt Tollet flying a Meteor F8 from Linton-on-Ouse was involved in a mid-air collision at 30,000ft and 14 days later Sgt Tickner used his Mk 1E seat from a Meteor FR9 in Germany when an instrument failure at 11,000ft resulted in the aircraft becoming uncontrollable. These two incidents brought some measure of comfort to pilots of No 77 Squadron Royal Australian Air Force who were flying the rugged but somewhat outclassed Meteor F8 in the Korean War, for it was certainly only a question of time before a member of the squadron joined the ranks of combat ejectees.

Performance comparisons between the MiG and Meteor did not favour the British aircraft but this did not deter the rugged and determined Australian pilots.

The Mk 1 Meteor had been the RAF's first operational jet fighter, entering squadron service in July 1944: the MiG, on the other hand, did not make its maiden flight until 2 June 1947 and was a much more advanced aircraft than even the Mk 8 versions of the British fighter that the Australians were flying. The arrival of the MiG-15 in Korean skies in November 1950 had marked the beginning of a new era in air combat. It soon established its superiority over the piston-engined F-51s and F-82s as well as the first generation jet fighters like the F-80 and F-84 then equipping USAF fighter squadrons. Not until the introduction of the first models of the famous F-86 Sabre in December did the UN forces have an aircraft of equal performance. The pilots of No 77 Squadron would dearly have loved Sabres, but the Americans had none to spare, and the British-designed and built Hawker Hunter, which it had been envisaged would be ready in time, failed to materialise, so the Australian government opted for the Gloster Meteor F8, the first of which arrived on the carrier HMS *Warrior* on 24 February 1951.

Comparison trials held between an F-86A and a Meteor in May 1951 quickly revealed that the American jet was much faster both in a steep dive and straight and level flight. However, the Meteor proved superior in turning ability and a sustained climb, which together with its heavier armament of four 20mm cannon — the F-86 had six 0.5 machine guns — made the Australians hopeful that they could give the MiGs a good fight.

UN's rules of engagement prevented any Allied aircraft from flying over the Yalu River into Manchurian air space, so the pilots could only fly to the border and wait. The enemy took advantage of this situation by only venturing forth when he had the advantage of height and numbers. On several occasions Meteor pilots watched MiGs take off, climb for height then turn back before crossing the border — it was a frustrating time for them. Even when the Meteors escorted B-29 Superfortresses to targets just on the southern side of the Yalu the MiGs failed to react.

First contact came on 25 August when a formation of Meteors flew air cover for US reconnaissance jets. The escort comprised two sections of four aircraft and it was Flt Lt Scannell, leading one section, who made the first contact. Ironically, Scannell was a New Zealander serving in the RAF who had arrived in Korea to help convert the Australians from the F-51 to the Meteor. He engaged a MiG with a burst of fire from his cannon, but the range was extreme and neither he nor his wingman were able to detect any hits.

Four days later the situation was to change dramatically. Sixteen aircraft operating from Kimpo, South Korea, were briefed for operations over North Korea, eight to escort American bombers, the others to carry out a fighter sweep between 35,000ft and 40,000ft in the area of Sinanju. In command of this two-section fighter sweep was Sqn Ldr Richard Wilson, leading 'Anzac Item' section of four aircraft, with Flt Lt Geoff Thornton leading 'Anzac Dog' section. WO Ron Gutherie, flying A77-721 (formerly WA954) in the No 4 position in Thornton's section, was on his 15th mission and like the other pilots was anxious to come to grips with the Russian-built MiG-15s flown by North Korean, Chinese and Russian volunteer pilots.

The eight Meteors escorting the bombers had an uneventful trip, but Sqn Ldr Wilson's formation, flying at 35,000ft, sighted six MiGs about 5,000ft above. He could see clearly their swept wings, squat shapes and red stars. Turning his aircraft to port, he kept a watchful eye on the MiGs. Then, noticing two more Communist fighters ahead and below, he decided to attack the lower bandits. Two Meteors winged over into a dive, but almost immediately the number two encountered compressibility and his aircraft entered a spin, which he was unable to correct until he reached 5,000ft. Wilson, unaware that his cover had gone, continued his attack. Flying at Mach 0.84 with the throttles wide open, he was closing the distance on the two MiGs when suddenly his aircraft shuddered as bullets found their mark. Wilson broke violently in a desperate attempt to shake off the MiG that had caught him in a classic tail attack. Fortunately his plight had been seen by the other two Meteor pilots who immediately dived on the MiG and caused it to break off the engagement.

The Australians were now surrounded by about 30 enemy aircraft; Meteors and MiGs swirled about the stratosphere in a gigantic dogfight. 'Anzac Item Three' was bounced by four MiGs but managed to avoid them as his wingman engaged four more without success. Suddenly the sky was clear of all enemy aircraft and Sqn Ldr Wilson was able to take account of the damage to his Meteor. The port aileron had been shot away and there was a hole, large enough for a man to fit into, in one wing. The main fuel tank had also been damaged and was leaking, casting doubts on whether or not he would reach home. He nursed the battered aircraft back to Kimpo at 25,000ft, was cleared for a straight-in approach, and had to land at well above normal landing speed. The Meteor responded to his every touch — if one lesson had been learned it was that the British jet could absorb tremendous punishment and survive.

Meanwhile, Flt Lt Thornton's section had also come under attack. The leader spotted enemy aircraft diving on them from the sun and quickly alerted his pilots. The four Meteors broke as the MiGs made their first pass, but when the Communist jets had been shaken off, a radio check revealed that 'Anzac Dog Four' — WO Gutherie — was missing.

At Kimpo the Australians took stock of the whole situation: and they had clearly come off second best. No victories could be claimed, one Meteor was missing and another was severely damaged. The arithmetic was bad but considering the odds had been about 4:1 against the Meteors and they had been at a height disadvantage, it could have been worse. Also, American Sabre pilots operating in the area reported they had seen a Meteor falling on fire as well as a parachute, so hopes for Ron Gutherie were high.

Gutherie had certainly borne the brunt of the attack. As the MiGs hurtled down on his section, he saw red tracer shells flashing past his wings. Breaking wildly to port he shouted a warning over his radio but, in the same instant, a cannon shell exploded in the fuselage of his Meteor destroying his radio equipment and preventing the others from receiving his call. Two MiGs flashed past in front and he turned in behind them: one came into his sights and his thumb pressed the firing button on the Meteor's control column. The four nose-mounted 20mm cannon burst into life and the smell of cordite drifted into his cockpit, seeping under his oxygen mask and setting his pulse racing. As he closed on the MiG his own aircraft suddenly shook and shuddered as 37mm cannon shells tore it apart; the concussion was such that he felt as though he had flown into a brick wall.

Gutherie had become another victim of a classic tail interception by two more

MiGs. The mortally damaged Meteor rolled on to its back and the MiG which had been in its gun sight only a few moments earlier banked away, seeking safety. The Meteor defied all Gutherie's attempts to control it: the elevator controls had been shot away and the rudder did not respond. It continued in a tightening spin to port and the pilot realised that his only course of action was to bale out.

Glancing at his instruments, Gutherie noted that he was descending through 38,000ft at Mach 0.84. He jettisoned the hood, then, reaching up for the face blind of the Martin-Baker Mk 1 ejection seat, he tugged it over his face.

All went well, the explosion hurtling the seat clear. Seconds later a drogue streamed out, stabilising the seat. This reduced the forward speed from over 500mph to zero until he was descending vertically in an upright position. As he descended he realised that his oxygen mask had been ripped from his face, but it was still attached to his helmet and when he pulled it back over his mouth, was relieved to find that his emergency oxygen supply was flowing through it. It felt odd to be just sitting in the sub-stratosphere without any apparent earthward movement even though in reality he was hurtling towards the ground at well over 100mph. The noise of combat, so thunderous seconds before, had gone, and there were no aircraft in sight. Far below was a vast panorama of land and sea. He seemed to be suspended alone in infinite space.

It was bitterly cold and Gutherie knew that the temperature was in the order of minus 50°C. There was a real danger of frostbite especially as he was wearing only a thin flying overall over his underwear and his gloves had been lost in the ejection. As he continued to fall he noticed that he was coming down towards the west coast of North Korea and it was possible he might end up in the sea — just what he hoped for because there would be a good chance that he could use his dinghy until discovered by one of the American air-sea rescue aircraft patrolling the area. The danger of coming down inland was that he would almost certainly fall into the hands of the Communists.

The only chance he had at this time of controlling his destiny was to detach himself as quickly as possible from his stabilised seat and use his parachute, over which he could exercise some control. On the debit side, this course of action meant that he would be exposed much longer to the intense cold. At an estimated height of 35,000ft the pilot decided that it was worth the risk, so he unstrapped himself from the seat, and kicked it away. His numb fingers found the ripcord and a sharp tug brought his parachute billowing from its pack. As the canopy fully deployed he saw the seat complete with its drogue chute falling well below and eventually vanishing from sight. Hanging in the shrouds he could see the curvature of the earth on the horizon and the jungle and sea spread below.

The cold was not as bad as he thought it might be and did not unduly worry him, and in any case as the minutes passed and he sank lower, the air became much warmer. Unfortunately a westerly wind was drifting him inland towards North Korean territory; the further he drifted in this direction the less his chance of recovery by friendly forces. Pulling on the rigging lines he tried to stop the drift but it soon became apparent to him that he was fighting a losing battle, and the best he could hope for was that he would land approximately 15 miles inland.

Descending through 10,000ft his wide horizons narrowed and features on the ground started to become more distinct. At 1,500ft he was startled by a new sound penetrating his world of silence . . . the zip and zing of bullets as Communist ground troops fired at him. The next few minutes were decidedly uncomfortable, but he landed unscathed in a paddy field 28min after he had baled out of his stricken Meteor. Discarding his equipment, the grounded pilot saw soldiers approaching from three different directions, and as there was no chance of escape he was taken prisoner.

WO Gutherie's comrades on No 77 Squadron did not find out the fate of their colleague until three months later when he was listed as a PoW in North Korea, where he was to remain for the rest of the war.

During his time as a PoW, WO Gutherie was promoted to the rank of Flying Officer, which accounts for why he is often incorrectly referred to by this rank at the time of the incident.

After the ceasefire in 1953, Ron Gutherie was repatriated and found that his bale-out had given him a unique place in history. He had been the first pilot to save his life in a combat situation with a Martin-Baker ejection seat, and secondly his high altitude bale-out was at that time the highest on record. He automatically became a member of the Caterpillar Club, founded by Lt Harold Harris, the Chief of the Flight Test Section of the Engineering Division of the US Army Air Service, who saved his life using an Irvin parachute on 20 October 1922. (The name 'Caterpillar' was chosen because at that time parachutes were made from silk.) Gutherie's 28min descent was at that time the longest in the club's history.

As he had strapped himself into his cockpit on 29 August 1951, Gutherie had no inkling of what was in store for him. The only piece of history which would have interested him was the recording of his first kill. He would have been far happier if he had caused a MiG pilot to have made the history-making high-altitude bale-out.

Another Australian pilot who was thankful that his Meteor was fitted with a Martin-Baker seat, was Flg Off Ken Blight who on 11 November 1951 used it to good effect to bring a satisfactory end to a fine piece of airmanship which might have been to no avail if the aircraft had not been fitted with an ejection seat.

Flg Off Blight was flying Meteor F8 A77-587 (ex-WA939) in the No 4 position in the leading flight of three returning from a fighter sweep in the Sinangu area. Just north of Pyongyang at 24,000ft and about 80 miles from his base at Kimpo, Flg Off Blight suddenly felt a tremendous thud which jarred the aircraft in a way that suggested he was on the receiving end of a 37mm cannon shell. His first thought was to call to his companions to break, but before he could do so the Meteor whipped into a gyrating dive which quickly developed into a spin.

The speed at which this happened shocked him into silence, but as is so often the case his brain reacted automatically and he started to reach for the ejection handle. Then his thoughts raced ahead and he quickly realised that he was still over enemy territory. Not relishing becoming a PoW, he decided to attempt to regain control of the aircraft. Fighting the controls brought no immediate response so his thoughts turned to the ejection procedures. But almost as quickly as it had started to spin, the Meteor momentarily stopped and wallowed into a semi-stable attitude. By winding on full left rudder trim and judicious use of the throttle controlling the inside engine, Flg Off Blight was able to keep some form of control and had time to take stock of his predicament. Looking out from his cockpit he was horrified to see that he had lost 4ft from his starboard wing; and almost as bad, on glancing back into the cockpit, he now noticed that the jet-pipe temperature (JPT) of the starboard engine was rising towards the end of its scale. He found that with full power on this engine and none on the port, with full left rudder trim and all the extra rudder he could physically apply, plus the control column held hard left and fully back, he could steer a reasonably straight course at 220kt, although he was losing height at 1,400ft/min. The slightest attempt to reduce power on the starboard engine, thus reducing the JPT, brought about a considerable loss of control.

He now pressed his R/T transmit button and called the other pilots of his flight, and discovered that the damage had not been caused by a MiG but by a midair collision with Sgt Robertson flying Meteor A77-959 (ex-WA909). Nine days earlier Sgt Robertson had been on the receiving end of some unwanted attention from MiG-15s, but had managed to nurse his aircraft back to base where the damage proved to be so bad that it was struck off charge. This time his luck had run out and following his collision with Flg Off Blight he was seen to spin down into enemy territory. Blight was still managing to keep some form of control over his Meteor and switched to the Kimpo emergency D/F and rescue frequency, requesting a course to steer for safety. The response was instant and he managed to edge round on to the approximate heading, but 2-3min later it began to look as though he was about to lose the unequal fight, so he retracted his gun-sight, depressurised the cockpit and opened the canopy with its electric motor. He called base again to check if he was over friendly territory, but it initially had some difficulty in locating the Meteor and it took 3min before confirmation was given that the aircraft had in fact crossed the front line. At last Flg Off Blight unlocked the seat, leaned forward and pulled the canopy jettison lever. There was a slight suction of dirt from the cockpit floor and the pilot looked up just in time to. see the hood flying about 20ft above the port side of the tailplane. Scanning further afield he could also see the base some 20 miles away on the horizon, and although his left leg was now numb from the unnatural exertion on the rudder bar, he decided that he could get a little closer — in fact thoughts of a crash-landing rather than an ejection even started to cross his mind, However, experimenting with his controls he found that even a slight change in their position caused the Meteor to roll, and the lowest speed at which he could keep any form of control was 190kt. Being unable to control the rate of descent, he therefore decided that to attempt to save the aircraft would be impossible, so he started to look for a suitable spot to abandon it. The best place seemed to be the coastal mudflats about seven miles northwest of Kimpo, but with his height now down to 5,000ft there was some doubt as to whether or not he could reach them.

A certain amount of anxiety concerning the actual ejection now started to enter his mind. He felt that the chances of leaving the aircraft cleanly were remote as every time he even relaxed on the controls the control column banged over to the right and the aircraft went into a spin. Having loosened his harness to reach the hood jettison handle, he now remembered to retighten it, and then checked he could easily reach the overhead firing handle. Once satisfied that everything was correct, he placed his right hand (with the palm inwards) above his head on the ejection handle, his right foot on the seat stirrup and jammed the control column to the left with his right knee. Quickly winding on nose-heavy trim, he simultaneously brought his left foot back to the seat stirrup and left hand up to the firing handle. With everything as ready as he could make it, he gave the firing handle a smart tug down with both hands. The result was instantaneous: he experienced a tremendous feeling of acceleration, followed by a peculiar sensation of deceleration with his legs flying out and flailing the air uncontrollably. (This was not an unusual situation with early ejections and led to the development of the leg restraint system.) The Mk 1E seat worked perfectly and soon the drogue had slowed it sufficiently for Flg Off Blight to consider his next action.

The seat was not oscillating nor did it seem to be descending at any great speed, so he was able to concentrate quite clearly on the necessary vital actions. Taking note of the position of his parachute 'D' ring, he took a deep breath, released his seat harness and kicked himself off. Separation was very smooth and although he started to tumble and felt uncomfortable as the wind hit his eyes, he was able to place his right hand firmly through the 'D' ring and pull it sharply across his body. In the following brief moments he saw the seat falling away and felt the canopy stream from its pack before a sharp jerk twisted his harness straps across the front of his face and jammed his head uncomfortably. This was only a minor moment of irritation for a quick tug at the harness saw the straps spring apart and left him hanging in the correct position beneath a fully deployed canopy. The ejection had taken place at 4,000ft at a speed of 200kt, so there was little time to admire the view from his lofty perch as WO Gutherie had done. Flg Off Blight landed in a paddy field and a few moments later was picked up by an American rescue helicopter and returned to Kimpo. A medical examination showed that apart from a few strains, a sore neck and bruised nose where the parachute straps had twisted, he was unhurt.

Without an ejection seat it is very doubtful if Flg Off Blight could ever have escaped from the Meteor by using conventional methods, because the moment he relaxed his hold on the controls the aircraft started to spin. There would have been no way he could have maintained some degree of control, whilst climbing out of his harness and battling with a 200kt slipstream to get out over the side.

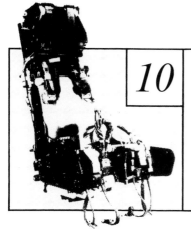

10 | Seagulls And Starfighters Don't Mix

The Lockheed F-104 Starfighter which first flew on 7 February 1954 was the first operational point-to-point interceptor capable of sustained Mach 2 speeds and faster; and although it held the world's air speed and altitude records simultaneously it is not events such as these for which it is best remembered. In the mid-1960s the Starfighter was never far from the front pages of the more sensationalist popular press mainly because of its apparently very high loss rate in the hands of the Deutsche Luftwaffe. The overall situation was not helped by articles from ill-informed journalists and the $20 million law suit brought against Lockheed by relatives of pilots killed in F-104 crashes. Careful analysis shows that in percentage terms the loss of F-104s in service with German air arms was not as great as with many other countries using the aircraft. For example, cumulative losses to 1967 were 17% in Canada, 11.3% in Italy and marginally over 8% in Germany; by comparison, cumulative losses by the USAF in 1956-61 (the first five years in service) were already 22%! In the immediate postwar period the RAF was criticised about Meteor losses and at one time there was a lot of hysteria generated about the seemingly high crash rate of the venerable Dakota.

Some of the German crashes did result from equipment failure and inexperienced pilots, but equally there were many unrelated to the type of aircraft. Nevertheless it was still considered by many to be a lethal aircraft, but in fact was one that was well liked and respected by those who flew it — though they pointed out that it was a high performance machine that needed to be handled carefully within its design limits and the capability of the pilot. After the sensational stories of the 1960s, the Starfighter 'scandal' gradually disappeared from the newspapers, and eventually if a F-104 did crash, it rarely made more than a few lines on an inside page. Such was the case with an incident that happened on 7 December 1982 which 15 years earlier would almost certainly have produced banner headlines.

On 6 December 1982 a pair of F-104Gs of No 322 Squadron 'The Flying Monsters', part of Jagdbombergeschwader 32 (JABOG 32), were briefed to fly a cross-country route that would take them from their base at Lechfeld to RAF Brawdy in North Wales, to Aalborg in Denmark and back to Lechfeld. Leader of the pair was Hauptmann Wolfgang Leuthner. His No 2, flying F-104G 24+97 (code number 8250), was Oberleutnant (now Major) Martin Dötzer, who at that time had 450hr experience on the F-104.

Martin Dötzer joined the Deutsche Luftwaffe in 1965 as a maintenance engineer but in 1977 volunteered for pilot training. After initial training on T-37 and T-38 aircraft at Sheppard AFB in Texas, he moved to Holloman AFB, New Mexico for advanced flying on the T-38A before returning to Fürstenfeldbruck AB in Germany where he flew the Fiat G-91. This was followed by conversion to the F-104 at Jever and then to Lechfeld where he still serves, flying the Tornado.

The two F-104s took-off from Lechfeld in perfect weather and as they climbed to operational altitude the clear blue sky formed a perfect backdrop for the breathtaking panorama surrounding them. Crossing close to London at 27,000ft, the pilots could see the coast of North Wales on the horizon, and it seemed like only a few moments later that they were dropping down to join the circuit and approach to Brawdy. That night both men renewed old acquaintances and made new friends with the pilots of No 234 Squadron, the resident unit at Brawdy. Wales is notable for its changeable weather, and when 7 December dawned the previous day's wintery sun had been replaced by strong cold winds, lots of mist and low cloud from which heavy rain fell almost continuously. The two F-104 pilots filed their flight plan, which they were forced to change several times as they waited for weather minima, sufficient for their flight to proceed, to be reached. On several occasions Brawdy was clear enough for them to go, but at their named diversions — Valley, Chivenor and Yeovilton — the weather took turns to fall below safety requirements.

The morning passed in weather-watching frustration but as noon approached the mist started to disperse and the cloud base increased; and a check with the Met Office confirmed that the alternates were also clear. With all limits within the required parameters, Air Traffic and the resident German Instructor at Brawdy, Hauptmann Herbert Hönig, gave the Starfighter pilots clearance to go. The F-104s taxied to the holding point, their long pointed noses nodding in unison as the pilots dabbed the brakes while they carried out final cockpit and pre-take-off checks. A final radio check confirmed that all conditions en route were still within limits, and the pair were cleared for a formation departure. The two General Electric J79 turbojets screamed to full power, and with afterburners switched on, over 15,000lb thrust pushed the fighters down the Brawdy runway and into the overcast at a speed that never failed to impress onlookers. The F-104s climbed very fast and both pilots had to carry out vital actions after take-off very quickly. The speed of acceleration meant that one of their earliest actions was to retract the undercarriage before reaching the speed threshold above which it was dangerous to fly with the wheels down. It was at this point that the first hint of trouble made itself known to Oberleutnant Dötzer. After selecting 'Gear Up' he saw that the three red warning lights had gone out but a red light on the retraction handle had started to flash. This indicated that the main and nose wheels had tucked themselves into the aircraft's fuselage, but the gear doors were down. He immediately advised the leader that he was unable to exceed the undercarriage down safety speed limit. Even at the reduced climb rate both aircraft had by now passed through 6,000ft and were flying totally on instruments (IMC).

Oberleutnant Dötzer recycled the undercarriage several times but still the red warning light continued to flash, a condition in which it stayed throughout the rest of the short flight. It was decided that the flight to Aalborg could not continue and a decision to divert to Cottesmore was made.

Left:
Maj Martin Dötzer and his crew chief. The aircraft is a F-104G similar to the type from which he ejected. *Martin Dötzer*

Below:
A F-104G Starfighter of FBW32. *Martin Dötzer*

The pilots changed their radio frequency from Brawdy to the London Military controller but soon lost direct contact; their calls were picked up by an RAF Jaguar pilot who then acted as a relay station. Despite this minor setback the two men decided that it was essential to find out the extent of the trouble, which could only be done by Hauptmann Leuthner carrying out a visual check on his No 2's aircraft. This proved to be more difficult than it sounds, for in the very poor weather conditions both pilots had their work cut out to fly close enough to each other for one to get a clear view of the underside of the other. It was particularly hard for Oberleutnant Dötzer because he had to constantly juggle with his power settings, watch his instruments, and recycle the gear whilst the leader tried to formate on him from below. The poor light within the cloud made it hard for both aircraft to stay within visual range but eventually the leader was able to confirm that the undercarriage had not cycled correctly and although the wheels had retracted the doors were still down. With no direct radio contact with London Military, both aircraft on IMC and one restricted to flying within a specified speed envelope, the pair decided to return to Brawdy and asked the Jaguar pilot to relay their request to switch back to the original control frequency. Clearance for this was quickly obtained and the controller at Brawdy relayed the weather conditions there to the Starfighters.

With zero visibility and cloud ceiling the report was not exactly encouraging, but the forecast was that this was one of the temporary lows that had delayed the original departure and it was expected to clear within 15min or so. The leader decided that it would be a good opportunity to give the Ground Control Approach (GCA) controller some practice in handling the F-104 since the approach speed of 250kt was higher than most aircraft he would handle on a day-to-day basis. After passing this request the two F-104 pilots decided to split the formation and operate as single aircraft to give each a chance of landing separately if the runway was sighted. Fuel reserves were no problem as each aircraft had enough for 1½hr flight time, and it was assumed that it was only a retraction malfunction that was causing Oberleutnant Dötzer his difficulty, so with his gear safely down he should be clear of any immediate problems. It was agreed that before splitting, the leader would check that his colleague's wheels were in fact safely lowered, but after selecting 'Gear Down', Oberleutnant Dötzer lost contact with his leader and was alone to sort out his problems. Advising Hauptmann Leuthner that he had lost visual contact he continued to assess the situation, trying to monitor his instruments with one eye and keep a look out to avoid a midair collision with the other. The aircraft's attitude indicator played an increasingly important role, and his eyes constantly fell on this, but as he carried out his continuous visual tour around the cockpit, his attention was suddenly focused on the rpm and EGT (Exhaust Gas Temperature) indicators which were now showing abnormal readings, in relation to the power settings, indicating that there was trouble with the engine as well as the undercarriage. There was no response to his attempts to recover the engine situation and he was now unable to speak with Hauptmann Leuthner as the GCA controller was blocking the frequency. The situation then started to deteriorate with alarming speed. Within the next few seconds the AOA (Angle of Attack) indicator went up and the air speed indicator started to unwind, confirming the pilot's fears that the F-104 was slowing down and getting very close to a stalled condition. The overall weight of the aircraft at this time meant that it had to be kept in the flying pattern at at least 250kt, and with 8,000lb of fuel remaining the stalling speed was in the order of 200-215kt, so the margin for recovery was very small. Flying at approximately 1,500ft above ground level the warning 'kicker' on the control stick started to become active, the AOA pecked above 5°, the VVI indicator started to move down and the speed fell to 190kt. Oberleutnant Dötzer decided that it was time to eject. He called his leader, 'Wolfgang I have to bale out', and heard the reply, '. . . was ist los Martl!' As he reached for the upper firing handle with both hands the last thing he noticed as he initiated the ejection sequence was that his position was radial 330/11DME out from the Brawdy Tacan.

Oberleutnant Dötzer heard a loud bang and felt a jolt as the cockpit canopy went and the seat fired. Total silence then surrounded him as he tumbled through the cloud and the seat stabilised as the drogue streamed. Separation followed immediately and he sensed the reassuring tug as his parachute deployed. Relief flooded through his mind as he carried out his post-ejection checks, although as he wryly says, 'At this time I was still in IMC so couldn't really see much of what was going on around me or my deployed parachute'.

The ejection took place at approximately 12.29, 29min after take-off from Brawdy. In that time the weather had changed several times and in the area where Oberleutnant Dötzer abandoned the F-104 the cloud base was 200ft, winds were west-southwest at 25-30kt gusting to 40kt, and the sea state was condition 3-4 — in plain language a very unpleasant day on which to be contemplating a dip in the ocean. Breaking cloud at 200ft Martin saw the white caps of the angry sea below him. The normal procedure when baling out over water is to try to release the parachute harness just before hitting the water, this preventing the occupant from being dragged through the water or the canopy collapsing over him with the resultant danger of being trapped. But it is very hard to judge height over water even when it is calm and especially when it is not in view for very long before impact. Hanging in his harness Oberleutnant Dötzer found it hard to assess his rate of descent or relationship to the surface, and he hit the water sooner than he expected. The wind immediately filled the canopy and dragged it and the Oberleutnant through the waves at a frightening pace. Face-down and trying not to take in vast amounts of water, Oberleutnant Dötzer struggled to find the quick release box, but every time he felt he was near it, a wave turned him over and his mad tumble through the water seemed to increase. Every so often he managed to gulp in a breath of air but the more he fought to turn on his back the more the sea seemed determined that he would not. The struggle between nature and man continued for what to him felt like minutes but were probably only seconds; after his fourth attempt he finally succeeded in reaching the release, turned it, hit it hard, and felt the harness release him from its relentless grip.

His life vest inflated automatically, rolled him on to his back, lifted his head from the water, and at last he was able to take some lung-filling fresh air. Quickly gathering his composure, Oberleutnant Dötzer manually inflated his life raft which had stayed attached to its lanyard throughout the mad gyrations and the tug of war with the parachute. Climbing aboard he was at last able to relax and take stock of his situation. Recalling his training in sea survival he checked his emergency equipment only to find that the aerial connection to his radio was broken. (The emergency radio which transmits a homing signal and can also be used for speech, is incorporated in the life vest and the aerial is contained in the vest's collar.) First priority was therefore to carry out a repair to the connection, although at the time he was not too sure how effectively this had been carried out. The stormy weather caused water to cascade into the dinghy so the next priority was to start baling, his helmet proving to be a more efficient receptacle than the bailer included. The water temperature was about 10°C and the wind was very cold but it was blowing in the right direction, so Oberleutnant Dötzer calculated that if his distress signals were not picked up he would be blown on to the Welsh coast in about 2hr — by that time very cold. There was little he could do other than to try to relax, keep warm and watch for search and rescue aircraft. The only sound was the wind, the sea and the crying of a lone herring gull which circled the downed pilot and which he looked upon at that time as his only friend in the world!

Some 20min after hitting the water he heard the unmistakable sound of a helicopter, and was delighted to see a Sea King HAR3 of 'B' Flight No 202 Squadron, detached to Brawdy for SAR duties, heading through the overcast towards him. Crewed by Flt Lt Norri Rough (captain), Flt Lt John Leech (co-pilot), Master Air Loadmaster Norman Pringle and Master Air Loadmaster Bill Payne, the Sea King was soon hovering close to the madly waving and much relieved Starfighter pilot. The winchman, Master Air Loadmaster Bill Payne, was lowered into the water and soon Oberleutnant Dötzer was on board where a doctor carried out a preliminary examination and confirmed that there were no major injuries. On landing at Brawdy a thorough medical examination, including extensive X-raying, was carried out, and as a matter of routine the German flight surgeon ordered a 24hr bed rest in hospital. Hauptmann Leuthner diverted to RAF Valley where he landed safely and was soon in touch with his rescued wingman, who was also quickly provided with a telephone line to his wife Eva to assure her and his two daughters that he was safe and uninjured.

Barely 3hr after his ejection and from his hospital bed, Oberleutnant Dötzer answered questions from the investigation team flown in from Germany, and that night No 234 Squadron arranged a party to celebrate the rescue and gave him the chance to thank the helicopter crew and rescue services.

The result of the investigation was not conclusive, but the findings indicated that soon after take-off the F-104 had been hit by some gulls which damaged a microswitch in the undercarriage retraction mechanism as well as the compression section of the J79, so the much maligned F-104 had flown for nearly 30min with a damaged engine. The Flying Safety Officer (FSO) at Brawdy found about a dozen dead seagulls at the end of the runway, which added weight to the birdstrike theory of the investigators, so perhaps the gull that befriended the lonely pilot in his dinghy was mourning his friends and saying sorry!

The ejection took place on Tuesday 7 December, and after a day in hospital and a day resting, a C-160 Transall of LTG-61 with the flight surgeon from Jabog 32 aboard arrived on 9 December to take Oberleutnant Dötzer back to Germany. The following Monday he was once again flying a F-104, carrying out what by coincidence was his annual check flight. As the Starfighter left the runway at Lechfeld, Oberleutnant Dötzer felt totally secure and reassured that he was flying a very good aeroplane, powered by a superb engine and fitted with an escape system that had worked to perfection.

11 | Death Of A Demon

Lt(jg) Charles T. Sylvester, the squadron material officer of VF31, sat in the ward room of the USS *Saratoga* enjoying his coffee and thinking about his forthcoming flight in one of the squadron's F3H-2N Demon fighters. He had joined VF31 four months before in December 1957 after a period flying the Demon with VF82 from NAS Oceana, Virginia. He was a fully qualified all-weather interceptor pilot and had close to 150hr logged on the McDonnell type, which had entered service with the US Navy in the mid-1950s after a troublesome gestation period. Charles Sylvester had slept for 8hr, taken a leisurely shower and enjoyed a breakfast of eggs, sausage and waffle washed down with coffee. He was totally relaxed and as ever looking forward to the thrill of flying a high-performance fighter on a Combat Air Patrol (CAP) which would in theory put another 150min or so into his log book.

Now fitted with an Allison J71 replacing the J40 which had been instrumental in difficulties experienced with earlier models, the Demon was a satisfactory if not outstanding aircraft and would continue to serve until 1965.

The aircraft assigned to Sylvester on 15 April 1958 was Bu No 13705, one of the last of a batch of 125 N2 all-weather versions of the Demon armed with four AIM-9C Sidewinders, delivered to the Navy. This particular aircraft had been accepted at St Louis on 16 March 1957 and had served with VF82 before being transferred to VF31 on 15 October 1957. The Allison J71 turbojet was a new one fitted on 4 March 1958 and had incorporated all modifications recommended by the manufacturers, including replacement fuel lines and the installation of a modified fuel pump.

On the day before Lt Sylvester's ill-fated flight, the engine had been removed to investigate and correct a fire warning discrepancy that had been reported. After completion of the work, fuel integrity checks were carried out and all feed lines checked for proper connection and security. The aircraft was filled with 11,500lb of JP-5, and a further hydraulic and fuel check was carried out through inspection door 34 by Lt Sylvester in addition to his normal pre-flight checks.

At 07.58hrs with all checks complete, the catapult strop in place and the engine running quite normally, Lt Sylvester secured his canopy and signalled to the launch officer that he was ready to embark on his mission. The next moment the Demon was hurtling down the deck of the *Saratoga* and climbing away on afterburn to its CAP assigned height of 30,000ft. Weather conditions were clear, and during the climb — made under visual flight rules (VFR) conditions —

Lt Sylvester busied himself with his post-take-off checks. He cleaned up the aeroplane aerodynamically, by retracting undercarriage and flaps, transferred 2,000lb of fuel from the drop tanks slung from their pylons under the wings, and changed his radio from the *Saratoga's* land/launch frequency to the combat controller's aboard the USS *Des Moines*. At 20,000ft he switched in the Demon's afterburner and made the last 10,000ft to his assigned altitude using the extra thrust this generated. For the next 40min the pilot flew a racetrack CAP pattern under the direction of the controller aboard the *Des Moines*, during which time he was given a practice interception and switched in the afterburner for about 2min whilst he successfully sought and engaged the imaginary intruder.

Some 15min after this, the controller asked Lt Sylvester his fuel state, which he reported as 7,000lb (5,000lb internal and 2,000lb remaining in the wing tanks). As his eyes swept the instrument panel to check this information they automatically recorded the positions of all the other needles and indicators, and he saw nothing to cause him any alarm. As a matter of routine he also checked the clock which stood at 08.47hrs which meant he had been airborne for 49min. Satisfied that all was in order, he settled back to concentrate on a new heading he had been given, but as he swung on to this he noticed that he was making a heavy vapour trail. He remembered from the weather briefing that he was not at contrail level, so immediately began to question why his aircraft had started leaving a tell-tale mark across the sky. A quick check of his instruments showed that the fuel gauge which moments before had shown 5,000lb internal (there was no gauge for the wing tanks) was now falling through 4,000lb. Depressing the transmit button on the Demon's control column, he advised the controller of his situation and asked him to vector him towards another Demon, also flying a CAP, so that its pilot could carry out a visual check, and at the same time requested a heading that would take him back towards the *Saratoga*.

Turning on to the new heading Lt Sylvester saw that his aircraft was still dragging a long trail of vapour, and the fuel gauge indicated that the internal level had now dropped to 1,800lb, this being confirmed by the flickering of the red light that indicated a low fuel level situation. Within seconds this turned to a steady glow as the fuel state reached 1,500lb. Lt Sylvester pressed his transmit button and urgently called into his radio 'Mayday, Mayday, Mayday', even as he did this he saw the fuel gauge register zero. For a few moments the engine continued to run normally, then it started to become very rough with the power fluctuating between 85%-95%; then, as various options flashed through his mind, Lt Sylvester saw that a fire warning light had come on to join the baleful stare of the fuel warning light. As he closed the throttle the pilot felt the engine finally flameout, and knew that he would need to call on all his skills to survive the next moments. Deciding there there might still be a chance of reaching the *Saratoga* and carrying out a dead-stick landing, he commenced setting up a glide pattern towards the carrier. Soon after shutting down the power he was relieved to see the fire warning light go out and saw that the engine was still turning over at about 12%; but the hydraulic power needed for the aircraft's flying controls was falling rapidly. When it reached 1,000lb/sq in he put out the ram air hydraulic pump, but was alarmed to see that the pressure in both systems was now reading zero, although the controls were still handling correctly and the Demon continued to fly normally. Instinctively he continued to pull the ram air pump handle as far back as he could — in his report he commented that he felt that he was bending it against its stop. Switching to 'Battery Only' and putting the ac switch in the inverted position, he saw that the hydraulic pressure gauges still recorded zero and decided that there was now no option other than to eject. During these events the aircraft had descended to 20,000ft with a 10-mile long fuel vapour trail dragging behind it. Lt Sylvester switched his emergency IFF on and gave another 'Mayday' call on the UHF guard frequency, before unclipping his radio and oxygen connections.

He decided that he would stretch the glide down to 15,000ft before ejecting, and on reaching this height used the emergency bale-out bottle to blow out the Demon's slats to reduce airspeed to 150-160kt. Pulling the nose of his aircraft up, Lt Sylvester reached for the face blind of the Martin-Baker Mk 5 seat and pulled the curtain over his face: the firing sequence worked instantly and he was aware of a push in his back then a rushing sensation as the seat left the aircraft. (The seat fitted to the Demon was the type introduced as standard into the US Navy in 1957. Martin-Baker developed it from the Mk 4 and it retained the standard 80ft/sec gun, 1¼sec time delay with a 'g' switch barostatic control, and duplex drogue. However, to meet American requirements, the seat structure and harness were strengthened to withstand deceleration loads of up to 40g instead of the 25g required in the British specification.)

Lt Sylvester has no recollection of separating from the seat: he felt himself falling and tumbling. He arched his back and the tumbling stopped, and then he found himself falling in a stabilised downward-facing position with his arms and legs splayed outwards: it was only then that he realised the seat had fallen away. His groping fingers found the 'D' ring of his parachute — a sharp tug, a slight jerk, and the canopy billowed from its pack and deployed. He estimates that he left the aircraft at 15,000ft and opened his parachute at 12,000ft. Taking stock of his situation he found that his Type H-4 helmet and oxygen mask were still firmly in place, as was (somewhat to his surprise) his knee clip-board.

Way below he could see the task group including the *Saratoga*, and decided to give them a guide to his position by releasing a daylight smoke flare from his life vest's survival equipment, at a height he estimated as 3,000ft.

On board the carrier Lt(jg) W. D. Dobbs sat aboard his helicopter watching the fighters being launched, unaware of the drama that was unfolding and in which he was soon to take a principal role. His reverie was broken as the hiss in his headset was broken by a short, urgent instruction to start his aircraft and take-off to stand by as an emergency was developing. Lt Dobbs and his crew reacted immediately and their helicopter was soon heading in the direction from which they were told a crippled fighter was heading back towards the group. Three minutes after departure, he noticed a Demon about two miles off his port bow. The aircraft was fairly low and seemed to be flying normally. As he watched, the fighter suddenly started to climb, then stalled and dived straight towards the sea. As it hit the water Lt Dobbs reported its position and headed his helicopter towards the point of impact. Another helicopter from the *Des Moines*, flying with Lt Dobbs, was directed to search off the starboard quarter for the pilot of the fighter. Both rescue crews were advised that the pilot had reported that he was ejecting, and as Dobbs's helicopter circled the area where the Demon had been seen to enter the water, the winchman's attention was captured by a smoke trail and he spotted a parachute at about 4,000ft, two miles off the starboard bow. Reporting the sighting to the controller, the pilot swung the helicopter on to an intercept course, then requested the other machine to join him in case additional assistance was needed.

Hanging in his harness, Lt Sylvester was able to watch the two helicopters below and as soon as they turned and headed in his direction, he knew that the smoke flare had served its purpose well. At 500ft he released the chest straps of his parachute harness and placed his hands on the fasteners of the leg straps. As soon as he entered the water he snapped open the fasteners of the leg straps, and, knowing a helicopter was hovering nearby, released the lanyard attaching him to his dinghy pack. The parachute harness and survival pack separated without any problem and in less than 1min he was secure in the rescue seat and winched aboard the helicopter.

As soon as his crewman spotted the smoke flare, Lt Dobbs headed for the most likely spot where the descending pilot would fall. He judged this to perfection, reaching the area about 15sec before Lt Sylvester hit the water. He hovered downwind at about 200ft and watched the sequence of events, reporting that the parachute remained billowed for about 6sec after the pilot hit the water. Waiting until he saw the pilot was free, he then moved in and lowered the rescue seat. Lt Sylvester was back on board the *Saratoga* some 75min after being launched on his mission.

When the Aircraft Accident Board (AAB) convened it concentrated its investigation in three general areas.

(1)   The pilot.
(2)   The aircraft and engine.
(3)   Aviation survival equipment and the rescue.

As items 1 and 3 were readily available a close examination resulting in concrete findings was possible. Unfortunately the Demon had crashed in deep water so no parts were recovered. Therefore findings could only be conjecture, but it is interesting to see just what was produced.

It was quite clear that engine failure was caused by an extremely rapid loss of fuel. Analysis of the pilot's report showed this to have been in the order of 2,000lb/min, so it was decided to look in some detail at the operation of the engine and airframe fuel systems.

A rupture of the fuselage centre fuel cell (tank) would result in complete loss of all internal fuel but allow the engine to continue running normally until it was empty, with fuel from the front and rear cells being fed by transfer pumps into the centre cell. A break in the afterburner fuel inlet line would also permit the operation of the basic engine during a rapid fuel loss as this line has pressure applied to it even when the afterburner is inoperative. There had been previously reported failures of this line but a modification to eliminate this had been carried out on the J71 of Lt Sylvester's Demon.

It was also noted that in the previous two years there had been several reported instances of failure of the afterburner pump housing. This too could have duplicated the symptoms of the fuel loss but again had been covered by a modification programme. Nevertheless, similar faults had been reported just a few weeks before the accident, so it was possible that there were other problems in this area. However, examination of the servicing records proved that the Demon involved had been modified totally in accordance with instructions. Looking further, failure of any component of the afterburner fuel system beyond the pump would not be likely to cause as rapid a fuel loss because the pump would not be operating and because the fuel lines were not large enough to handle the volume at boost pump pressure.

The final conclusion published by the AAB in respect of the aircraft and engine stated.

'A rapid loss of fuel, 5,000lb in approximately 2-3min occurred in F3H-2N Bu No 13705 after one hour of normal operation. The exact cause or origin of the fuel loss cannot be determined as the aircraft was lost at sea and no parts were recovered. However, analysis of known factors involved in this accident, as well as past history of the J71 engine, leads the board to believe that the most probable cause of the fuel loss was a rupture of the afterburner fuel inlet line or the afterburner fuel pump. Cause of such a rupture is undetermined since all lines were believed installed properly and given all known field tests and checks prior to flight. As was stated in the investigation, rupture of the centre fuel cell would cause this accident. However, for such a large amount of fuel to drain from the fuel cell so quickly the fuel cell housing itself would had to have been ruptured; there is no evidence to support this conjecture.'

The AAB recommended that the Bureau of Aeronautics conduct additional tests of the afterburner fuel inlet line and afterburner fuel pump housing of the J71 engine in order to determine whether the service modifications had been adequate solutions to previous malfunctions. Every item of Lt Sylvester's survival equipment, apart from his exposure suit, performed its designed task and the AAB felt that the following general points about the ejection were worth highlighting:

(a) The pilot slowed to 160kt (IAS) before ejecting.
(b) His H-4 helmet (old type), oxygen mask and knee board were retained throughout the ejection, descent, and rescue.
(c) The quick release leg and chest strap openers enabled the pilot to free himself quickly from his parachute after entering the water.
(d) An arched back, arms out, legs out position was used to stop tumbling before pulling the ripcord.

As far as the exposure suit was concerned, Lt Sylvester had been in the sea less than 1 min so had been surprised to find that his underclothing was wet from the waist down which appeared to indicate that his immersion suit had leaked. It was found that this had been manufactured in May 1957 and issued three months before in a new condition to Lt Sylvester, who had worn it on approximately 12 flights. Close examination revealed a small tear near the lower right base of the portal canopy seal. The size and position was not adequate enough to explain the amount of water that had entered the suit, so more tests were carried out. The suit legs were filled with water, and as this rose above the boot top it began to seep rapidly through the fabric on all sides in a band about 4in wide. A further area of penetration was also found in the lower posterior thigh and back of knee areas. These areas were all located in places where the suit was subjected to maximum flexion and abrasion. Visual inspection of the inner rubber surface brought to light a series of small ¼in fine cracks, all of which coincided with the leakage sites. A check on all the squadron's suits showed no similar problem, so there was clearly no general design or material fault. As a result of the one-off occurrence it was nonetheless recommended that regular immersion tests and inspections of the interiors of all exposure suits should be carried out.

Commenting on the rescue, the AAB described it as '. . . routine in all respects and was effected after the pilot had been in the water approximately one minute. The fact that Lt Sylvester lit one of the smoke flares during his descent through 3,000ft of broken cloud enabled personnel from the ships and rescue helicopters to locate him expeditiously'.

Lt Sylvester had of course handled the emergency in a most accomplished and professional manner and this brought him due credit from members of the Board.

Charles Sylvester is now Consul General in Shanghai, and he looks back on 15 April 1958 with typical understatement, 'Ejections from the F3H did not always go as well as mine. I remember being wildly elated at various stages in the sequence because I was still in one piece'.

Below:
Test ejection of a Mk 5 seat from a Demon. *Martin-Baker*

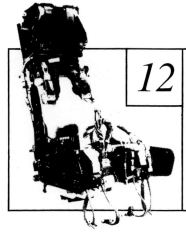

12 A Close Shave For Jo

Joe Dell enjoyed working on the night shift. It suited him to return to his home at Long Itchington, Warwickshire, when most people were getting up to start their day. He would have a few hours' sleep, then potter in his garden, listen to the radio, pop along to the local shops or just take the air. On 30 May 1949 he had enjoyed an afternoon in his garden: the warm sun polished the clear blue sky and held the promise of a good summer. As he packed his tools away he noticed that clouds were beginning to gather; by the time he went indoors to prepare for work, they covered nearly half the sky and brought a distinct coolness to the afternoon. One of Joe's nightly rituals was to shave before he reported for duty, and he had just lathered his face and was about to apply his razor, when a strange sound caused him to look out of the window of his council house. He saw a parachute descending close to a nearby canal, so, still clutching his razor, he rushed from the house and went to the aid of the parachutist.

Joe Dell and several other witnesses on the ground, did not realise that they had seen history being made, for the man to whom they now headed was test pilot John Lancaster — known to his friends as Jo from his initials J. O. — who had just had the closest shave of his life.

John Lancaster served an engineering apprenticeship with Armstrong Whitworth Aircraft before the outbreak of World War 2, during which time he had been involved in work on the Whitley bomber. Despite — or maybe because of — his close association with bomber aircraft, he wanted to fly fighters once he had completed his pilot training. But it was not to be.

After training at No 5 FTS he was posted to No 20 Operational Training Unit (OTU) at Lossiemouth and learned to fly Wellingtons, an aircraft for which he formed a deep affection and on which he completed his first operational tour. A period of instructional duties followed and he then flew the famous Lancaster on a second tour. Next he was posted to the A&AEE at Boscombe Down in 1943 where later he was to join No 3 course at the Empire Test Pilots School (ETPS), from which he graduated in 1945. He left the RAF as a Flight Lieutenant in January 1946 and for a short period joined Boulton Paul before becoming deputy to Geoffrey Tyson at Saunders-Roe. Under the guidance of Henry Knowler the Saunders-Roe team had been working on the design of the SRA1, a flying boat fighter which was one of the first of the new postwar jets to be fitted with a Martin-Baker ejection seat from the outset. The prototype made its maiden flight on 16 July 1947, some four months before the aircraft in which Jo was to make his historic escape, and seven months after he and Geoffrey Tyson had experienced the ejection seat rig at Martin-Baker's works.

Pilots who had been used to sitting on their parachutes in a bucket seat held firm by the traditional Sutton harness were not too worried about their ability in an emergency to roll the aircraft on to its back and fall out, or slow it down and dive over the side, they viewed the ejection seat with some suspicion. Of course, a lot of them had read about aircrew in the war being trapped by centrifugal force and only escaping when their aircraft broke up, and had realised that for every occasion this happened there must have been some who were not so lucky — but surely this was part of flying and the risks that one accepted?

Sitting in a seat attached to an explosive charge was at that time naturally viewed by both air and groundcrews with a certain amount of suspicion. So it was with some reservations that Geoffrey Tyson and Jo Lancaster made the trip to Denham on 1 January 1947 to see, and perhaps try, the test rig at Martin-Baker. Both men had been weaned on the democratic system favoured by the armed forces, so Geoffrey Tyson, being senior, was first to be strapped into the test rig and fired up it. The sight of him ascending put serious doubts into Jo's mind about the need to have a go. However, he decided that he ought to, and after his test shot found that he was in some pain in the area around the base of his spine. His local GP concluded that he had perhaps 'bruised his spine a bit', and for several months Jo suffered a certain amount of pain which gradually receded — but an occasional twinge reminded him of his short vertical trip.

After a short period with Saunders-Roe, Jo Lancaster rejoined Armstrong Whitworth. Chief designer, John Lloyd, had in 1942 designed a wing section that played an important part in laminar flow and boundary layer research as applied to flying wing aircraft. This was a configuration that for many years had represented a challenge to aircraft designers. It has often been claimed that postwar British and American flying wings were based on those designed in Germany during the war and fully documented in captured documents.

No doubt the postwar availability of captured documents was useful, but as both British and American designers had also been tackling the problem since the early 1940s, it is grossly unfair to dismiss their projects as stemming from German research. The truth is that any set of designers faced with solving a similar problem are almost certain to arrive at the same conclusions.

Wind tunnel tests on the laminar flow wing indicated that full-scale testing was essential and this was carried out on a Hurricane. In the meantime, to prove the basic aerodynamics of the design, proposed for a jet bomber powered by four Metro-Vick Beryl engines, it was decided that Armstrong Whitworth should build a flying wing glider. Much experimental work into laminar flow and boundary layer control with the Hurricane and a Meteor — outside the scope of this work — confirmed John Lloyd's views that a flying wing would derive most benefit from this system. It was decided therefore that a model should be built.

Maiden flight of the AW52G, RG324, took place in March 1945 with Charles Turner-Hughes at the controls and the last Whitley built by Armstrong Whitworth as the tug aircraft. This two-seat glider was two-thirds the size of the two proposed powered versions of the flying wing.

Gas turbine engines — two Rolls-Royce 5,000lb thrust Nenes for one and a pair of 3,500lb thrust Derwents for the other — were chosen for the powered aircraft as these allowed a high degree of suction to be available for boundary layer control. It was realised that control of the 'wing' across a very wide speed envelope would be difficult to achieve without boundary layer control; but with it, air that would normally swirl around the wingtips at low speeds, causing them to stall, would be smoothed out by sucking it inside the wing through slots.

Like any tailless aircraft the elevators and ailerons (elevons) of the AW52 were combined along the trailing edges. The rudders on both the glider and powered versions were mounted vertically at the tips.

Jo Lancaster carried out several flights on the AW52G, which was of wooden construction and torsionally very stiff. It was limited to fairly modest air speeds so there were never any flex-induced vibration problems with it.

The Nene-powered AW52 (TS363) was ready for taxying trials in April 1947 and these were carried out at Baginton and Boscombe Down where the aircraft was moved for its maiden flight. Much of this work was carried out by Eric Franklin who quickly discovered that the longitudinal control was inadequate. Modifications were carried out and the aircraft's first 'hop' confirmed the prediction that the elevators were very sensitive. The maiden flight was made by Eric Franklin on 13 November 1947 during which it was found that very small movements of the spectacle-type control column, initiated fore-and-aft oscillations at about two cycles per second. Subsequent flights brought to light other control problems including the induction of rapid pitching oscillations at low level which diminished as the aircraft climbed into calmer air. By December 1947 the aircraft had accumulated several hours of useful flying, during which a flight test-observer had noticed wing flexing; this may have been contributory to a vibration that had been experienced at an airspeed of 250mph (knots at that time were not in fashion!). Overall the controls of the aircraft were poor, one pilot reporting that they lacked harmonisation, were spongy, and longitudinally were far too sensitive. These were views confirmed by Jo Lancaster when he joined the test programme.

The second aircraft, TS368 with Derwents, joined the test programme in September 1948, just in time for the SBAC display at Farnborough where it was displayed in the static park, the flying demonstration being carried out by TS363. The first aircraft underwent considerable structural modifications to stiffen it up torsionally, following which the limiting speed was increased from 300 to 350mph. While this work was being carried out flying continued with the Derwent-engined TS368, and it was found that this aircraft had the same control problems which tended to be even more evident due to the lower power which limited its performance envelope. In March 1949, Bill Else was flying this aircraft with an observer, and as he climbed away from a low-level pass over Baginton, flown for the benefit of Armstrong Whitworth employees who had not seen their product in the air, he encountered turbulent conditions which immediately brought on oscillations as experienced in the Nene-powered AW52. Reducing speed to 280mph, he regained control. Initial reaction was that flutter of a trim tab or control surface had caused the problem, but the pilot had not noticed any excessive control inputs so this theory was dismissed. Test instruments recorded readings of +12g to −4g so TS368 was grounded for a full structural check. How the frequency and amplitude of this experience compared with those that Jo Lancaster experienced in TS363 during his later eventful flight no one will ever know, but it was assumed that the Derwent's sortie was unlikely to arise with the Nene-powered machine because of the airframe stiffeners. We shall see that this assumption was not entirely accurate.

Designers had been aware for some time that control inputs would eventually need to be power assisted, and a variety of experiments in power controls were being carried out. The problems experienced with flutter and resonance were not limited solely to tailless aircraft like the AW52 and DH108 — at Saunders-Roe the SRA1 was grounded after a few hours flight time to enable scientists at RAE Farnborough to carry out their resonance tests. They finally recommended a slight change to the elevator tab balance: this was carried out, but on the flight following this, Geoffrey Tyson experienced elevator flutter from take-off to landing, so they reverted to the original design.

On the AW52, in order to make lateral control at all manageable, the elevons had to have very weak spring tabs and a spectacle-type control column. The result was that laterally it handled like a Lincoln whilst longitudinally it was like a Spitfire. If full power controls had been available the aircraft would no doubt have been very pleasant to handle. Nevertheless, in flight the AW52 was very flexible and there is little doubt that it was this flexibility, coupled with the weak spring tabs and very small fore-and-aft control movements, that created major problems.

Jo Lancaster joined the programme on 3 May 1949. His first flights in the Nene-powered machine were aimed at giving him familiarisation and general handling experience, and were scheduled to incorporate a gradual increase in air speed beyond 300mph. His first flight on 23 May lasted 35min and enabled him to get the feel of the aircraft and its control characteristics.

This was followed two days later by a 45min sortie which eased the path of progress towards the higher speed envelopes. Then on the afternoon of 30 May 1949 he was briefed to take the AW52 to beyond 300mph IAS. It was a bright, blustery day with towering cumulus clouds building up to cover about four-tenths of the sky. Such conditions were typically accompanied by turbulence and Jo made a mental note of this as he prepared for take-off. There was nothing eventful in the climb away from the airfield and soon the flying wing was in bright sunshine at about 5,000ft. For 20min or so the pilot busied himself with routine checks and tests, then started a gentle descent allowing the IAS to build up to around 320mph. Without any warning a violent fore-and-aft oscillation set in, inducing considerable symmetrical wing bending, which within 2-3sec built up to a very great amplitude. The pilot's instinctive reaction was to attempt to throttle back, but so violent was the oscillation he almost immediately became incapable of any reasoned recovery action, if indeed any such action was possible. The AW52 was out of control: Jo Lancaster, now an unwilling passenger, was only concerned with getting out before he was rendered unconscious.

The aircraft's designers had carefully considered the problem of escaping using the ejection seat and had incorporated an emergency control which fired explosive cutters to sever the control circuits, and included a spring which moved the control wheel fully forward as the canopy was jettisoned. The handle for this was alongside the canopy jettison lever on the instrument panel. Clearly initiation of this vital circuit was rather final, so a safety split-pin was incorporated through the operating handle to prevent accidental operation; very few pilots ever considered removing this split-pin before flight! Jo Lancaster was no exception: in the predicament he now found himself it was impossible to remove the pin so he had no choice other than to pull the hood jettison and then the face blind to initiate the ejection seat. As the AW52 continued its attempts to turn itself inside out, Jo was becoming more and more disorientated and confused. He reached out, placed one hand on the hood jettison, the other on the face blind, and pulled both simultaneously. In his controlled but hurried actions he forgot to withdraw his feet into the seat's footrests, but this proved to be a bonus because in the position he left them his legs scraped past the 'spectacle' grip with only slight bruising.

When the stability problem hit the aircraft it was flying at 5,000ft, and by the time the ejection sequence had been initiated it was down to 3,000ft. Recovering his wits after his exit from the cockpit, Jo found himself leaning forward in the seat at an angle of about 45°. The drogue had automatically deployed and stabilised the seat so the next action was to release himself from the seat and operate his parachute. The harness was quickly unfastened and he rolled forward out of the seat, pulling his parachute ripcord as he fell free. The parachute streamed from its pack, deploying fully as air entered the canopy. As it checked his descent the pilot saw the seat falling past, still trailing its drogue. Taking stock of his surroundings Jo realised that the stiff breeze had induced a large amount of drift and it became apparent to him that he seemed to be heading for a ducking in a canal.

Recalling his RAF parachute instructions, he tried to steer himself away from the canal, but all he achieved was to initiate an enormous swing, so he quickly abandoned this attempt at controlling the canopy. The parachute continued to swing with the drift and he landed fairly heavily, being dragged through a hedge to within 5yd of the canal before he managed to hit the quick release and free himself from the harness. Standing up he came face to face with local farmer Mr Shepherd and Joe Dell, whose lather-covered face served as a subconscious reminder of the close shave he had just had. The farmer took him to his house from where he telephoned Baginton, then relaxed with the obligatory cup of tea to await collection.

The ejection and subsequent landing resulted in overall bruising, a large chip off the top of the right shoulder bone, as well as two compression fractures in the base of the spine. An X-ray revealed that the 'severe bruising' diagnosed after the test ejection at Denham 2½ years before, had also caused two compression fractures. General opinion was that the spinal fractures had resulted from Jo leaving the AW52 with his feet unsupported, but medical science showed that he had in fact unknowingly suffered the same injury in the test rig even though he was in the ideal ejection position with legs and feet supported on that occasion. If he had managed to pull his feet back into the rests prior to initiating the ejection sequence, he could well have suffered very serious injury from the control wheel which he had not been able to move into the safe ejection position. Later, static tests in which he was winched out of the cockpit of the other AW52 indicated that even with his legs in the position they were at the time of ejection, he had been very lucky to escape past the spectacle control without injury.

A rather amusing sequel came in the August when Jo faced a medical board at the RAF's Central Medical Establishment (CME) in London, for examination to determine his fitness to continue test flying. He met the requirements of the examination but on the Medical Inspection Report given to him on 8 August 1949 there is a note under assessment which states: 'FIT/Civilian Test Pilot (M.O.S.) but not to be exposed to hazards of Martin-Baker ejector seat.' This is rather like telling a sailor that he can go to sea again providing the ship is *not* fitted with lifeboats.

The day after the ejection the national press had a field day, for not only were they able to describe graphically the loss of a top secret Flying Wing aircraft (sic) but also reveal to the world that the pilot was the first man to save his life in an emergency using a Martin-Baker seat. As would be expected, some claimed this to be the first ever emergency escape using any form of ejection seat, and as is usual in such reports the pilot's injuries ranged from a sprained wrist to serious cuts and bruises. As for the AW52, this was reported as having flown on pilotless for several miles before hurtling to earth at 400mph, skimming treetops before breaking up and spreading itself across many acres of land. After the ejection the AW52 had regained some measure of stability but crash-landed some two miles away, tearing out its engines on impact. The ejection seat was found about half a mile away from where Jo landed.

Jo Lancaster returned to test flying, but what was the ultimate fate of the remaining AW52? After the crash of its Nene-powered twin, TS368 was grounded. It did not fly again until October 1949 when it was subjected to a test programme which included vibration measurement, using sophisticated (for the period) equipment, and subject to a speed restriction of 250mph. On completion of these tests it went to the Aerodynamics Flight at RAE Farnborough where some laminar flow experiments were carried out, but in the main it served as a curiosity and was sometimes flown just for the experience of piloting a flying wing. Eventually it was struck off charge and broken up into several large pieces for scrap. History has it that the scrap dealer who bought it collected it on several lorries one Saturday morning; and at the same time local based army units were holding manoeuvres, the overall result being a monumental traffic jam the likes of which had never been seen before.

Thus even in its death throes the AW52 left a legacy to be remembered. In America the Northrop experiments also came to an abrupt but tragic end. Just six days after Jo Lancaster's ejection the YB-49 jet bomber wing exploded suddenly over Muroc killing all five crew, and on 15 March 1950 the second aircraft did exactly the same. Although a bomber based on the design had been ordered into production and subsequently changed to a reconnaissance role when it proved to be a poor release platform, the order was cancelled in April 1949. In October 1951 the remaining YRB-49A was scrapped, thus bringing an end to the American venture into the flying wing configuration in favour of the more conventional B-36.

Nevertheless, like the AW52, Northrop wings made their own contribution to history. One had flown for 9hr 30min, covering 3,458 miles at an average speed of 382mph at between 35,000 and 40,000ft. One was also recorded for posterity when it was used in the film adaptation of H. G. Wells's novel *The War of the Worlds*, where it depicted a bomber of a future air force attacking Martians.

In the early 1950s there was hope that the flying wing would prove to be the right way forward. Nearly 40 years on it still seems very unlikely, but developments in aviation have an odd way of reviving the past and producing an interesting future. Whether or not this will be the case with such designs remains to be seen, but one thing that was certain in 1949, and which started with the AW52, was that aircrew could escape in total safety from a doomed aircraft by using an ejection seat, which in 1949 was a device from the pages of science fiction, but which is now a standard and essential piece of equipment for every military aircraft.

Below left:
AW52 TS363 from which J. O. Lancaster made his historic ejection. *AWA*

Below right:
After J. O. Lancaster's ejection, tests were carried out on the other AW52 (TS368) at Bitteswell to discover how he escaped without serious leg injuries. Here he is strapped to the seat and being slowly winched from the aircraft. *AWA*

Bottom:
The medical certificate issued to J. O. Lancaster after his ejection. *J. O. Lancaster*

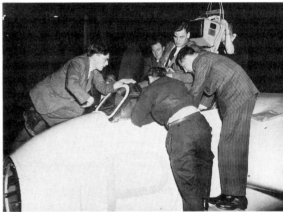

CONFIDENTIAL

MEDICAL INSPECTION REPORT

R.A.F. Form 624

Date 8th August 19 49.

Official No.	Rank	Name and Initials	Whether a defaulter or if for duty	Disease	Medical Officer's Remarks	Disposal
	MR.	J.O. LANCASTER.				
		Examined at No. 1 C.M.B. for continued fitness for duty as test pilot of M.O.S. aircraft.				
		Assessment :-		FIT / UNFIT Civilian Test Pilot (M.O.S.) but not to be exposed to hazards of Martin-Baker ejector seat. Review by Orthopaedic specialist in 6 months.		

* Strike out whichever is not applicable.
† State nature of duty for which warned.   In the case of men for medical inspection the reason, such as "joining the station," etc., should be stated against their names.

Orderly N.C.O.'s Signature ....

Medical Officer's Signature .... S/Ldr.

Assistant President No. 1 C.M.B.
ROYAL   AIR   FORCE.

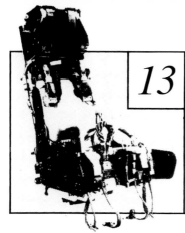

13 | The Will To Survive

There was a loud and distinctive explosion in the cockpit of the A-6A Intruder. The pilot, Lt Jim Molinski USN, had no sensation of pain but he knew something was wrong and that his aircraft had been hit. He pulled back on the stick to climb out of the target area, then passed out.

'You're climbing too high!' A startled shout from his navigator/bombardier, Lt Chuck Wilson USN, was the next thing Molinski recalled. He opened his eyes and found that the aircraft was indeed climbing a little too high. Grabbing the stick he rolled the A-6 to starboard, at the same time pushing the rudder to swing the nose in the same direction. As the controls responded he pushed the stick forward to get the nose down and headed in the direction of the coastline. As the Intruder dropped to a more acceptable flight level the pilot realised that his navigator, sitting alongside him under the huge bubble canopy, did not realise they had a major problem. He pressed his intercom transmit button but found that for some reason his companion could not hear him, so tearing his oxygen mask — which contained his microphone — away from his face, he shouted to him that he had been hit. Chuck Wilson looked anxiously at the actions of Molinski then realised that his pilot was in trouble. Keying the transmit button on the UHF set he called the carrier, told them that the pilot had been hit but that the aircraft was still flying, and asked them to stand by for further transmissions. He then asked Molinski how he was and received the reply: 'I'm doing fine. I don't feel too hot — there's something wrong. I've been hit but I don't know where.' Molinski located the source of pain as somewhere under his left arm. He was afraid to look because he thought that he may have lost the whole arm, but knowing that he could not pretend nothing had happened and he could not put off the moment forever, he glanced down. With growing relief he saw that his hand was still intact, but it was draped over the throttles and try as he might he could not will it to move. Wilson passed Molinski a heading of 100°, which would take them back to the carrier, and told him, 'Hang on and just keep me informed as how you feel.'

Both men realised that there was a vast difference between keeping the A-6 in the air and putting it down safely on the heaving deck of their ship — but this was a problem for the future.

The Grumman A-6A Intruder is a rugged all-weather attack aircraft powered by two Pratt & Whitney J52 two-shaft turbojets. Despite its heavily loaded weight — which is more than double its empty weight, and considerably more than most World War 2 bombers — it has superb low-speed handling qualities because of its full span slats and flaps. The two-man crew enjoy excellent all-round vision from the large

128

bubble canopy, and the navigator has access to very comprehensive navigation, radar and attack systems, which were integrated into Digital Integrated Attack Navigation Equipment (DIANE). Capable of operating in all conditions, Intruders worked around the clock in Vietnam making pin-point attacks on targets that were beyond the capabilities of other aircraft, only being relieved from this role when the F-111 arrived on the scene. The aircraft carried its weapons on underwing pylons, and was fitted with a pair of Martin-Baker Mk 5 seats.

Molinski and Wilson had successfully attacked their target and were leaving at low level when ground fire had hit their aircraft. At this stage Molinski could not detect any major problem with the airframe or controls, and the A-6 seemed to be responding quite normally. Realising that a deck landing might be difficult he asked Wilson to work out a course for a diversion airfield on land because he felt that between them they had a better chance of landing successfully on a metalled runway. Soon after crossing the coast, the pilot felt waves of nausea passing over him and started getting that flushed feeling which normally precedes unconsciousness. Turning to his navigator he said, 'I'm not feeling very good. I don't think I'm going to get much further.' Wilson had other ideas. Reaching into his flight suit he produced a small bottle of medicinal brandy that he said he carried for just such an occasion, and a swig from this cleared Molinski's head and immediately made him feel a lot better. He now felt refreshed enough to discuss the forthcoming landing problem with his navigator. Explaining that he could not use his left hand and this would therefore lead to unacceptable risks in attempting a deck landing, he suggested that if they could reach a land base, he could operate the throttles with his right hand whilst the navigator controlled the aircraft with the stick.

Course and distance to the nearest diversion was calculated but once again nausea started to overtake the pilot, so this action was abandoned and they decided after all to head back towards the carrier, which was positioned south of them and in flying terms not too far away from the diversion selected. If they reached the carrier they would be doing well; if they encountered a problem en route they could still divert; and even once beyond a decision point they still had another diversion lined up that they could reach if the carrier was moving about too much for an attempted deck landing. They therefore called control aboard the ship and advised their decision, heading, fuel state and overall condition.

A few minutes later Molinski once again started to feel very bad, and decided that it was unwise of him to risk the life of his navigator any longer. He told Wilson that he thought there was no way he could make it to the ship and therefore had decided to slow the aircraft and prepare to eject. All the options were again considered and Wilson agreed that the decision was right since it gave both men a much greater chance of survival. The navigator took control of the aircraft and held its wings level as the pilot leaned across to operate the throttles with his right hand. Reducing power to about 80% and putting out the wingtip speed brakes, Molinski then took the control column back from Wilson's grasp and continued to fly the aircraft. As the speed fell off he felt increasingly weak, and realised that if the bouts of nausea continued at the rate they had reached, he might have a problem in the actual ejection. He had no wish to delay this too long because he feared losing consciousness and drowning. It was therefore of paramount importance that he retained some control of his senses so that he could set himself up as soon as he was in the water. At this time he still had no idea exactly where he had been hit or how serious his injury was, and there was still no show of blood to give him a clue.

By this time the airspeed had fallen to 225kt, and Molinski advised Wilson that he was now feeling really bad and to stand by for the ejection. He asked if Wilson remembered his ejection procedures and received an affirmative reply. Both crewmen should have cross-checked the drill of vital actions between them, but in the heat of the moment they overlooked this as they were very occupied in transmitting their position and setting the aircraft up in the best position for the actual ejection. As the speed decayed to 220kt Molinski warned Wilson that he was about to jettison the canopy, which separated quite cleanly from the aircraft. The rush of air into the cockpit temporarily revived the pilot, who told Wilson to delay his ejection as he felt he could now hold on a little longer. But within a minute he once again felt he was slipping into unconsciousnes, and yelled to Wilson, 'I'm going to pass out. Eject! Eject!'

To prevent further injury to his damaged left arm when he ejected, Molinski had reached over with his right hand, picked up the left one, wrapped it around his lap strap and trapped it between his legs. He now turned to look at his friend and saw him give the thumbs up sign, point towards him then gesticulate upwards. The whole cockpit seemed to be spinning, and just as his vision started to cloud over, he recalls reaching up and pulling the face curtain of the ejection seat. He has no recollection of anything else until he found himself floating in the sea.

Subconsciously he must have carried out all the correct drills, but he can only vaguely remember pulling the lanyard that actuated the CO_2 bottle which inflated his Mk 3C life vest. His parachute must have been freed at exactly the correct moment for he recalls bobbing to the surface as the life vest inflated, and immediately being revived by the water. Looking around he could see no sign of either his parachute, the navigator, or the aircraft. He guessed that either his companion had ejected much later than he had and was therefore some way from him, or had entered the water at the same time and was hidden by the waves; although the sea was calm, at eye-level the slightest swell tended to hide even fairly large objects. As he rose and fell on the gentle swell, he suddenly recalled one word mentioned during the briefing officer's outline of local conditions in the event of an emergency.

'Sharks.'

The officer had advised crews that reports of everybody's big fear had been received. Molinski was particularly concerned as he knew that he was bleeding, but still was not certain to what degree or how serious his wound was. His priority now became to get into his life raft as quickly as possible. This would automatically have been ejected with him and be held on a lanyard below his legs as he descended. With his good arm he reached down to locate the strap and to his horror found *that he had no life raft*.

Sometime during the ejection the whole seat pan had detached itself from the pilot's personal equipment connector. He concluded that he had not made the connection before take-off, but his mind told him that this could not be so, since it was second nature. In any case, on the odd occasion when he had not made the connection it had been immediately apparent to him that something was wrong, and a further check had been carried out. Another reason to believe he had connected the Harley buckle was that if the seat pan had come off during ejection it had to slide off his legs and past his feet, and with his body in the ejection position it would have made scratch marks on his boots or even bruised him: neither was the case. It seems likely that his damaged left hand, which he had tucked into his belt, pulled up the lap strap when the parachute opened and released the whole assembly.

Whatever the cause there was little that Molinski could do. He was in the water, bleeding and with no life raft. Looking around he saw that his parachute was floating close by about 4in under the water. His concern about sharks took precedent over all else, and contrary to everything he had been taught about getting away from the empty parachute to avoid being tangled in the canopy and shrouds, he decided that if he could get on top of it, then pull it around him, he could contain any blood in the parachute and it would therefore not attract marauding sharks. After a short struggle he managed to get into position and was horrified to see the water turn crimson against the white backdrop of the canopy. Almost immediately he began to get tangled in the lines, and it took only a few seconds for him to realise the soundness of the message conveyed in training, so he quickly abandoned the idea and swam away. Molinski was the safety officer of the carrier's A-6 Air Group, so probably knew the survival procedures and equipment better than any other crew member.

Nevertheless, now faced with reality rather than theory, he found it extremely difficult to locate the flares and shark repellent stowed in his life vest with one hand — in practice they had been easily accessible with two. After about 5min of pushing, prodding and pulling inside the Mk 3C life vest he located the repellent and managed to tear the container open with his teeth, then surrounded himself with it. Now feeling slightly more secure he started to swim, believing that a trail of dispersing blood was better than a pool gathering around him. Probably making him feel even more secure was that during the struggle to find his life raft and survival equipment Molinski had become aware of the squadron's commanding officer's A-6A orbiting above him at about 1,000ft, so he knew that the crew had him in sight and rescue must only be a matter of minutes. After 15min or so he saw two Douglas A-1 Skyraiders and a search and rescue Albatross approaching. As the trio drew near the A-6 rolled out of its tight orbit and flew towards the Albatross, then turned back and started to orbit again . . . but this time some three miles away.

What had happened was that the crew of the A-6 had seen Molinski eject and his aircraft crash. They also heard the navigator talking to them on his radio from the safety of his life raft, and assumed that only he had survived and that the injured Molinski had gone down with the aircraft. In fact both men had successfully ejected close together, but the navigator had gone out on their blind side and they never saw his descent. They were therefore only looking for one person in the water, and in locating Molinski then picking up the navigator's radio transmission they thought they were dealing with one and the same person. Thus when they returned to circle the survivor after breaking off to gain visual acquisition of the Albatross and communicate with its crew, they found Wilson and thought they were looking at the same person they had been orbiting originally. Suddenly the sky was filled with aircraft, as the rescue operation moved into top gear, helicopters and another Albatross joining the original trio circling about three miles away from Molinski. All fear of sharks disappeared as he realised what was happening, and his priority became to attract them to his position. His own words adequately describe his dilemma:

'I was all by my lonesome, feeling pretty bad about the whole situation and had to start thinking how I was going to let somebody know where I was. The first thing I looked for was the Mk 13 Mod O day/night signal flare. I pulled one out and realised right away that I was going to have a hard time igniting it with only one hand. I thought of trying to do it with my teeth but immediately dismissed that idea. I thought of putting the flare under my dead arm next to the Mk 3C and pulling it with my right hand, but was afraid to do that for fear that it would burn a hole in my life vest which was the only thing keeping me alive. So finally I decided to put it between my knees under water and pull the cap off, then try and hold it above the surface. I pulled both ends — the ring on one end just snapped off and the other peeled off the way it's supposed to but it didn't ignite. I was very disappointed that I couldn't get either end to work.'

Despite the continuing frustration confronting him, Lt Molinski was not the sort of man to give up easily. He now turned to his PRC-49 radio which was rigged in a canvas bag and attached by a strap to his body.

With his one good hand, Molinski was faced with a tremendous struggle to push his survival pack away from the bag containing the radio and, when he had done this, to extract it from its canvas container. He wrestled with the radio for about 5min and when he at last got it out, was shattered to find that he could not hear the signal indicating that it was working. Selecting the transmit position he called the rescue aircraft and advised them that he was in a straight line south of their position and asked them to acknowledge. The stony silence told its own story. He tried again but it was quite clear that the radio was not working speech transmit so he tuned it to the position which it would transmit a continuous 'bleep', tucked it under his right arm and held it on top of his life vest.

The noise of engines directed his gaze overhead where he saw another pair of A-1s heading for the group already circling some three miles away. Amongst his personal equipment Molinski was wearing a 0.38 calibre pistol which was armed with ball ammuniton because he believed that if he needed it, it would be to shoot somebody, and that if it was required in a survival situation he would have time to reload with tracer which he also carried. He nonetheless decided to fire at the A-1s to try to attract their attention. Although at the time he thought the crews might hear his shots, he realised later that above the noise of their engines this would have been impossible. However, the will to survive pushes men to desperate measures, so he aimed at the aircraft and fired four shots when they passed overhead at about 700ft. There was no sign of acknowledgement, and his frustration increased to a level where he thought he should aim to hit the aircraft with the remaining two shots. Realising that this would not solve his problem, he fired the last two under the starboard wing of one of the A-1s, but, as he knew in his heart, this had no effect and the pair flew serenely on.

Next he decided to try to attract attention with tracer. He groped for the ammunition, found it, then as he struggled to hold the pistol under his right arm to re-load he dropped it. The pistol should have been secured to a lanyard, but as he tried to retrieve it he found that either in the ejection or his contortions in the water, the lanyard had been cut and the pistol was now gone. Worse, during the approach of the original A-1s he had waved his white helmet to attract their attention then attached it to his life vest, but now to increase his troubles that too broke loose and floated away. He was slowly losing every piece of survival and signalling equipment he had.

Molinski now tried to find other pieces of equipment that he knew were stored within pockets of his life vest, but the handicap of only having one usable arm made this very difficult. It was difficult to push things around his body to find extra flares that he knew were stowed somewhere. At last he found his pencil flare gun, which he had earlier looked for, but it had been tucked beneath a lot of other equipment. Now his fingers closed over it and he gripped it very tightly as he pulled it from its stowage and screwed a flare into position. Watching the two A-1s, he waited until they turned, and when they were heading towards him he fired the flare. It arced into the sky right across the path of the two Skyraiders: they immediately levelled their wings, made minimal adjustments to their track and headed straight towards him. Had his luck changed at last?

To his great relief the aircraft made straight for him, and when they were more or less overhead he fired another flare, and saw them start to circle. By the time a third flare was loaded a helicopter was approaching, and just to be absolutely sure Molinski fired this. The helicopter dipped in acknowledgement and was soon hovering over the now very happy A-6 pilot. The loss of his hard hat and visor meant that Molinski now had problems keeping the helicopter in sight for the spray thrown up by its rotors hit his face and eyes like a thousand pin-pricks. He was anxious to see if the crew were lowering a collar or seat. He thought, 'If he lowers the seat, I can probably get myself up with one hand, but I don't think I can hook myself up with a horse collar.' Squinting up he saw that it was a horse collar that was being lowered, but was soon aware that a crewman was being lowered to assist. He felt an arm supporting him and connecting his torso harness to the collar, then saw that the man helping was his navigator. Having already been plucked from the sea by the same helicopter, Lt Wilson had insisted that the crew lowered him back into the sea to help his injured pilot. Secure in the harness Molinski was hauled into the helicopter and the collar was then re-lowered for the navigator, but to avoid delays he waved it away so that the injured pilot could be taken immediately to a nearby cruiser.

Another helicopter arrived on the scene and soon Wilson was swinging from the rescue seat for the second time within 20min. Both men were reunited aboard the cruiser and Molinski's wound, which turned out not to be as serious as he had at first thought, was treated. The next day they were flown to the carrier and later were assigned a period of survivor's leave.

It was found that no transmissions were received from the pilot's radio, but as the navigator's had functioned perfectly correctly and transmitted distress as well as voice transmission, it must be assumed that Molinski's had suffered damage when he was wounded or during the ejection. No official report has been released for publication. As far as Molinski was concerned, he owed his life not only to the ejection seat, but mainly to his resolve not to give up the quest to survive when at times it must have seemed easier to just lay back in his life vest and accept what fate had in store. When all else had apparently failed the small flare gun proved to be his saviour, and therefore it is not too surprising that he summed this up: 'The pencil flare gun is worth its weight in gold as far as I am concerned. In future I'm going to carry about twice as many cartridges as I ever carried before.'

(At the request of the United States Navy the names of the crew have been changed and the squadron and ships involved not named. But the incident is factual and occurred off the coast of Vietnam in September 1966.)

14 | Double Trouble

Eject! Eject'

The two words shouted by Flt Lt Paddy Mullen of No 14 Squadron echoed into the headset of his No 2, Flt Lt Stephen Griggs, who seconds before had been quite happily flying straight and level in Jaguar GR1 XX963, but was now fighting to control his wildly rolling aircraft.

Stephen Griggs had no idea what had happened. Having just satisfactorily completed a fairly uneventful 1hr sortie, he was concentrating on holding his position just behind his leader, when the world went mad and his aircraft appeared to explode and commenced to gyrate all over the sky. Deciding that his leader knew something that he did not, Flt Lt Griggs watched the spinning kaleidoscope of sky and ground, and when the sky appeared in the right place, pulled the firing handle of his Martin-Baker Mk 9 seat and ejected. At that time he had no idea that he had been involved in a remarkable accident that was eventually to make headlines in the world's press, and that less than four months later was also to become a member of that elite band of men who have saved their lives twice with ejection seats.

On Friday 7 May 1954, almost 28 years to the day before Stephen Griggs's first ejection, Sqn Ldr G. Storey of No 56 Squadron found himself in difficulties whilst spinning a Supermarine Swift. The aircraft, which was destined to have a short but eventful career with the RAF, was a contemporary of the famous Hawker Hunter and had been heralded as the last word in swept-wing fighters when it entered service with No 56 Squadron in February 1954. It was the first British-designed swept-wing jet fighter to serve with the RAF and the first to have power-operated ailerons — but enormous operational problems were soon encountered.

No 56 Squadron's joy soon turned to frustration and a longing for the return of its obsolete but reliable Meteor F8s or issue of the Hawker Hunter. Eventually the Swift was withdrawn from the interceptor roll and No 56 had the questionable distinction of being the only squadron to operate the aircraft as a point-to-point interceptor.

The teething problems of the Swift were uppermost in Sqn Ldr Storey's mind when he found that he was unable to recover from his aircraft's spin. Therefore at 10,000ft and an estimated IAS of 200kt he became the first RAF pilot to use the new automatic Mk 2E Martin-Baker seat from a Swift. The sequence operated perfectly and soon after leaving the doomed aircraft he reached for the override handle, but at this point the automatic sequence functioned, separating him from the seat and deploying his parachute.

134

Nearly one year later, on 19 April 1955, the Squadron Leader, now the Commanding Officer of No 56 Squadron, was flying from Waterbeach in company with Capt C. G. Gillespie, a USAF pilot on exchange with the RAF. The shortcomings of the Swift had now led to its withdrawal and No 56 Squadron had been temporarily re-equipped with Meteor F8s, a retrograde but somewhat welcome step as far as the pilots were concerned. At 7,500ft the two Meteors touched, each one losing its tail in the collision and entering a spiral dive from which recovery was clearly impossible. Sqn Ldr Storey reacted immediately and although 'g' forces made it difficult for him to reach the overhead firing blind, he managed this at about 5,000ft and ejected through the aircraft's canopy. Once again the automatic seat, which by then had been fitted to Meteor aircraft in a modification programme, operated perfectly.

Afterwards Storey reported that immediately he left the aircraft the seat stabilised; so smooth was the separation that he felt he was being gently lifted out of the seat, and was a little surprised to find that he was still wearing his helmet, oxygen mask and sun-glasses. Capt Gillespie remained in his aircraft a little longer, eventually leaving it at 3,000ft. He too had an uneventful escape and, again, according to his report, 'was most impressed and somewhat surprised at the efficiency of the Mk 2E seat'. On this occasion both seats were fitted with the 24in diameter drogue and not the duplex drogue. This was another double success for Martin-Baker, and in the case of Sqn Ldr Storey, a place in the history books.

However, the distinction of being the first military pilot to save his life using a fully automatic Martin-Baker seat belongs to another double ejectee, Lt C. R. Bushe RN of 800 Squadron Fleet Air Arm. Flying from HMS *Eagle* on 15 May 1953 off the coast of Northern Ireland, Lt Bushe heard an explosion in the engine of his Attacker FB2 which immediately caught fire. Not too surprisingly his reaction was immediate: he jettisoned the canopy, pulled the face blind and left the aircraft at about 1,500ft and 250kt. Other members of the formation reported that the Attacker was banking to starboard in a nose-up attitude, and was already beginning to break up as the ejection occurred. Lt Bushe estimates that from the time of the explosion to the time of the ejection, about 4sec elapsed. He ejected with his feet in place on the rudder bar, and used only one hand to pull the face blind, but cleared the cockpit without any form of injury.

For about 3sec he descended attached to the seat and its drogue then he became aware of the separation sequence, after which he became slightly alarmed when there appeared to be a delay in the opening of his parachute. This was probably very insignificant but in such circumstances a few seconds feels like minutes. The seat parted cleanly and he had ample time to fully prepare himself for his entry into the water. Release from his harness, inflation of his dinghy and rescue by helicopter all went like a dream and a very relieved Lt Bushe was quick to praise the Mk 2A seat he had used.

Two years later, on 12 September 1955, he was again to be thankful to the team at Denham. He was flying a Wyvern, again from HMS *Eagle*, sailing off the Scottish coast near Cape Wrath. Joining the circuit with wheels lowered and flaps down, he was in a gentle turn at 200ft with an IAS of 200kt when the aircraft's ailerons started to give trouble. He found that he was unable to correct a very right wing low attitude, so breaking off his approach he carried out a spiralling turn to starboard. Reaching 800ft at 130kt it became evident that the problem was becoming worse so once again he reached up for the face blind and pulled it hard. Apart from the boots being torn from his immersion suit during the ejection, there were no problems. He estimates that by the time he had descended to 400ft his parachute was fully deployed, and he was plucked from the sea — which he reported as being 'very very cold' — within 2min. Lt Bushe had become one of the early double ejectees and commented that he hoped not to have to use the seat for a third time, although he did add as a rider to his report that 'it might be fun to try the *new* Martin-Baker seat in the future!'.

In the month before Lt Bushe's second ejection, Flg Off Hedley Molland of No 263 Squadron based at Wattisham, also destined to be a double ejectee, made history when he ejected from his Hunter Mk 5 (WN989) at 25,000ft at an indicated Mach 1.1. It was fortunate that he was so high because although his True Air Speed (TAS) was around 760mph, his Indicated Air Speed, which determines the degree of air blast, was about 480kt. The Hunter was not a supersonic aircraft, its maximum speed in level flight being in the order of Mach 0.93, but in a shallow dive from altitude it could exceed Mach 1.0, a feature which was an attraction at air displays before the supersonic bang created by breaking the so-called sound barrier was banned.

On 3 August 1955, Molland was in a pair of aircraft that had climbed to 40,000ft to carry out practice interceptions on each other. After 10min of this the leader called for a tail chase. Molland acknowledged and the chase was on. Both aircraft were still at 40,000ft with Molland some 400yd behind the leader flying at full throttle at an Indicated Mach Number (IMN) of 0.86, when the leading Hunter went into a steep turn to port. He then straightened out and started a full-throttle dive of about 30°. Molland, still about 400yd to the rear, dived his aircraft and was soon touching Mach 0.98. He had just experienced the customary slight forward movement of the stick associated with reaching that Mach number when the leader started to pull out. He tried to follow but although he pulled the stick back to the limit of its travel, the Hunter's nose would not rise. The nose in fact began to drop and the 23-year-old pilot felt himself being lifted slightly from his seat by negative 'g'. Immediately he trimmed full nose up from the half-division nose down he had set before starting the tail chase. He then throttled back but this had no noticeable effect on the angle of dive. At 25,000ft with the stick fully back, the aircraft diving at between 70° and 80°, it was quite clear that something was seriously wrong with the Hunter's power controls and recovery was impossible. So, releasing the stick, Molland put his right hand on the hood jettison release and his left on the ejection seat blind handle. The hood went cleanly and the air blast swept in, sucking his maps and other loose oddments out of the cockpit. The force of the blast caused his vision to fade so he quickly pulled the blind with his left hand and did not bother to pull his feet back off the rudder bar. The last he saw of the Mach meter it was registering Mach 1.1. He heard the seat fire, felt himself spinning through space and then blacked out. Recovering consciousness he found that he was sitting upright in the seat and, looking up, saw the drogues streamed out. His left arm was twisted round the side of the seat and he made several unsuccessful efforts to pull it back. Each time it blew round the side of the seat again and in the end he decided to let it stay where it was. During the ejection Molland had lost his left shoe and sock, helmet, oxygen mask, both gloves and his watch which had been on his left wrist. All three dinghy leads had become detached but he managed to reconnect one of them with his right hand before separation occurred at 10,000ft. There was a jolt as his parachute opened and soon afterwards he noticed a circle of foam on the sea where his Hunter had crashed. Taking stock of his surroundings he worked out that he was going to land some miles off the coast near Felixstowe. Unable to swim, he took no chances and inflated his life jacket whilst still at some height. After splashing in he bobbed to the surface and within a few minutes was picked up by a tug, a crew member from which dived into the sea to help. Later he said that although he had always been comforted by the thought that the seat was there if needed, he didn't think he stood a great chance of escaping at the speed he was travelling. The two actions required at that time to jettison the hood and then operate the seat had led to many discussions in the crew room about the amount of turbulence that would be created once the hood had gone. It was felt that this might well lead to difficulty in ejecting, so Molland and his fellow pilots had spent some time practising the technique of operating the hood jettison with one hand and the seat blind almost simultaneously with the other. This worked for him but the one-sided pull on the face blind resulted in his left arm, instead of lying in front of his chest, pulling to the left and being blown around the side of the seat and fractured. His legs too were separated by the ram effect of the air blast and the forceful abduction injured his left hip joint and pelvis. Other injuries consisted of minor bruises including a black eye and small haemorrhages in the eyelids. However, the Mk 2H seat had worked to perfection and after a period in hospital Hedley Molland, who at the time of his first ejection had 40hr on Hunters, returned to flying.

Ten years later, on 29 September 1965, now a Flight Lieutenant, he joined the double ejectee club when he abandoned his Lightning, F3 XP739. The Lightning was the only British-designed and built Mach 2.0 fighter to serve with the RAF, so it is somewhat ironic that whilst piloting a transonic Hunter, Hedley Molland ejected at above Mach 1.0 but when flying a fighter that could easily surpass this speed in level flight, he was travelling at about 250kt but very much lower.

Making his approach into Wattisham and with five miles to run to the runway threshold, both engines on the Lightning flamed out. The pilot immediately took to his ejection seat and landed safely at Chapel Farm, Stoniham, whilst the Lightning flew on for a while then crashed at Battisford.

The two ejections by Flt Lt Molland occurred at opposite ends of the speed and height ranges, but Luftwaffe pilot Maj Hans-Joachim Zabler became a double ejectee from almost identical situations, and the same type of aircraft. On 24 January 1984 he was flying a TF-104 from the back seat and after completing a low-level exercise requested permission to stay in the circuit and carry out some touch-and-go landings. Air Traffic authorised his request and he carried out two successful landings and overshoots. The third landing was completed but as the aircraft gathered speed for take-off, the pilot felt it lurch and strike the ground very heavily near the end of the runway. Since there was no chance to recover he gave the command to eject. Simultaneously the pilot in the front seat had also made the same decision and both men left the damaged Starfighter together. It subsequently proved impossible to tell whether the sequence had been initiated by the front or rear system, as apparently both were applied at exactly the same time. Both men escaped with minor injuries, Maj Zabler's being a broken bone in his right foot caused when he landed on a pile of frozen snow.

The Court of Inquiry found that a sudden cross-wind had hit the aircraft at the point the gear was retracting, forcing it to strike the runway and seriously damaging the underside of the fuselage.

Nine months later, on 19 October, Maj Zabler was again flying a TF-104, this time on a transfer flight from Ingoldstadt to Memmingham. On this occasion the back seat was unoccupied. The flight was uneventful, as were the approach and landing: after touch-down the braking parachute was streamed, and the Major concentrated on keeping the aircraft on the runway centre-line. The nose wheel dropped into contact with the runway, and as this happened there came the first indication of trouble. Despite Maj Zabler's efforts to steer it, the aircraft started to cavort from left to right. Still travelling at some speed it finally headed for the edge of the runway and once again the Major decided to eject. On this occasion there was no frozen snow to mar the final outcome and he was totally uninjured.

At a dinner to celebrate the landmark of 2,000 lives saved by Martin-Baker seats, held at the London Hilton Hotel on 10 May 1968, of the 217 ejectees present, 13 had two escapes to their credit. At the time of writing over 5,200 have been saved of which several hundred are double ejectees, and four are triple. A record of four ejections — all from F-4 Phantoms, the last being a Royal Navy aircraft during an exchange posting — belongs to Lt D. J. Lortscher USN, a Weapons System Operator. Unfortunately he was later killed when he and his pilot failed to eject from an F-14.

Returning to 25 May 1982, Flt Lt Griggs was a weapons instructor at RAF Brüggen in Germany carrying out 'Standeval' (Standard Evaluation). In this capacity he could fly with any of the four Jaguar squadrons based at Brüggen as a fully operational pilot. On 25 May he had chosen to fly with No 14 Squadron and as already mentioned was flying a Jaguar GR1 (tail code 'AL') as No 2 to Flt Lt Paddy Mullen, an experienced member of the squadron. The pair carried out a forward air control sortie in Northern Germany and were completing their exercise with a standard low-level recovery to Brüggen. The two Jaguars were flying in arrowhead formation, with Stephen Griggs at an angle of some 45° to Paddy Mullen's starboard and trailing by some 40 to 50yd. Both men were aware that as part of the continuous need to keep all NATO aircrew alert and on their toes, it was not unusual for any RAF Germany aircraft to be treated as hostile and subjected to practice interceptions by NATO machines operating on QRA (Quick Reaction Alert).

Therefore it came as no surprise to Flt Lt Griggs when, as he and his colleague approached the Wesel area in the region of the POL (petrol, oil and lubricants) depot, he picked up a radar warning receiver signal indicating that he and Paddy Mullen may have been intercepted from the front quarter. The indication then moved to the rear quarter. At this time the pair were under control of Clutch Radar which had not advised them that there was another aircraft in the area. As the warning information moved to the rear, Stephen Griggs became a little confused and decided to carry out a visual search behind his aircraft. This proved to be unproductive so whilst staying aware that there might be a hostile aircraft in the area he decided that the signal could also be coming from something on the ground — although his instincts and experience warned him that this was unlikely.

Meanwhile, at RAF Wildenrath, Phantoms of No 92 Squadron had been loaded with live weapons in accordance with normal policy for exercising quick reaction of air defence forces in NATO. For the purpose of such exercises other RAF Germany aircraft were regarded as hostile. Aircrew participating in the exercise were briefed regarding the prescribed safety precautions for the carriage of live weapons, such briefings being intended to prevent accidental firing.

Phantom FGR2 XV422 took off from Wildenrath to mount a combat air patrol (CAP) under the control of a Sector Operations Centre (SOC). Soon after take-off the crew carried out their pre-attack checks during which the air-to-air missiles were armed. At this time the navigator, who was engaged in other tasks, did not monitor the pilot's actions and was therefore unaware that his colleague had rendered live one of the two main safety switches.

At approximately 12.47hrs the Phantom's navigator detected a radar contact which the pilot identified as a pair of Jaguars. In accordance with the exercise scenario they decided to engage the 'hostile' aircraft. Following standard procedures for a simulated attack, the Phantom closed on the Jaguars and when in an ideal position to complete what until that moment had been a typically routine engagement, the pilot pulled the weapons release trigger.

When inert training weapons are carried, this action should simply produce a witness mark on a film record. Prior to this action, the Fighter Controller on the ground who vectors the interceptor on to the target, should ask the crew to check their arming. In this incident, various factors, including some misleading inputs into the aircraft's on-board systems, combined to disrupt the normal procedures. Thus when the pilot of the Phantom operated the firing sequence the growl from one Sidewinder transferred on to the other and a live missile was launched towards the Jaguars.

The AIM-9G Sidewinder entered or struck the starboard (No 2) engine of Stephen Griggs' Jaguar, exploded and blew the complete rear end off the aircraft. It was quite coincidental that at the precise moment of impact Paddy Mullen happened to look behind to check on the position of his Number 2. As he did so he was horrified to see the Jaguar explode for no apparent reason. His immediate reaction was to press his R/T button and tell Stephen Griggs to eject. It is even more remarkable that this transmission reached the pilot, since the Jaguar's communication aerial is housed in the tail, which the missile had removed. What probably happened was that a small piece of the aerial wire was left on the aircraft's fuselage and this was sufficient to pick up the frantic call.

The Jaguar pilot's reaction was immediate. He recalls that he was bent over double at the time and therefore not in an ideal or recommended position for ejection. As he left the aircraft one knee struck his chin causing a small cut, but his most vivid memory of this moment is seeing the cockpit floor rapidly disappearing beneath him. Automatic separation occurred at once and his next recollection is of hanging below his fully deployed parachute. He carried out his post-ejection drills but as the escape happened at comparatively low level (1,300ft), by the time he had completed these he was very close to landing. A slight problem was encountered in finding the fastening for his Personal Survival Pack (PSP) which on release hangs on a strap beneath the ejectee, so the total descent was made with this still attached to Flt Lt Griggs' rear end. The parachute did not gyrate and no tumbling was experienced, and soon after having the opportunity to take a look at his surroundings and notice that he was floating towards a field close by a river, he landed with the PSP still firmly in place. The presence of this equipment caused no problem and he managed to release himself from his parachute, and remove his helmet. First on the scene was Gerd Mölleken, the farmer in whose fields the remains of the Jaguar and its intact pilot had landed, and a young girl. Mölleken shook Stephen Griggs warmly by the hand and in very broken English wished him a happy birthday! It later transpired that 10 years before a Harrier had also crashed in the same field and Gerd had helped the pilot untangle himself from a tree in which he landed after a safe ejection.

Standing in the field with his would-be rescuers, Stephen Griggs was mystified as to what had happened and asked the farmer if he had seen anything that might help solve the mystery. He seemed to understand the essence of the question, which he answered with a negative shake of his head. At that moment Paddy Mullen flew over to check on his No 2, and as Stephen waved to confirm that he was OK, he saw that a Phantom was trailing the Jaguar. It crossed his mind that Phantoms did not often fly as singletons, and he immediately began to worry that he might have had a mid-air collision with the companion of the one now following Paddy — perhaps one of the pair he was sure he had picked up on his radar just a few minutes before. Gerd Mölleken confirmed that he had not seen any other aircraft involved in the incident, then took Stephen Griggs to his house where he gave the pilot a large brandy. Soon afterwards the German fire and police services arrived to cordon off the area and Flt Lt Griggs was able to contact Brüggen to advise them of the situation. A rescue helicopter took him back to Brüggen from where, after a quick chat with the Station Commander and the OC Ops, he was taken to the RAF hospital at Wegberg for X-rays and a check on his back. All was pronounced well and he returned to Brüggen, where by now the story had been pieced together, and he was advised that he had in fact been shot down by a Sidewinder.

It seemed only right to celebrate his escape in the traditional manner by laying on a barrel of beer, which also acted as some form of acceptable compensation to No 14 Squadron for the loss of one of their Jaguars. During the downing of this the crew of the Phantom arrived to offer their apologies, although at that time neither they nor Stephen Griggs were really sure just what had brought about the chain of events that led to the ejection.

It is quite possible that the whole incident might not have received the publicity it eventually attracted if Dr Uwe Jens, the local SPD member of Parliament, had not received reports from his constituents who said they had seen the aircraft disintegrate and expressed concern about how close the wreckage had fallen to the BP refinery at Bucholtwelmen. Investigation of the crash had been handed over to the RAF and initially all the MP's questions to the authorities met with the answer 'No comment'. This however did not stop local gossip, which was claiming that the Jaguar had been shot down by a Sidewinder missile, a fact that was reported in the magazine *Flight* in England just four weeks after the event. After seven months of probing by the MP, the Bonn Ministry eventually confirmed the story which was given prominence under the headline *Aircraft Crash — Bonn States British Man Shot Down His Comrade* by the *Rheinishe Post* in its 18 December 1982 edition. After detailing the MP's quest for information and giving a somewhat dramatised version of the part played by Gerd Mölleken, the paper added: 'The German Ministry of Defence wrote to the SPD MP saying, "The shooting down of the Jaguar was without doubt caused by human error" (sic). The investigation has apparently not been fully completed. The Royal Air Force assure us, however, that measures have already been taken to avoid a repetition of this.' The statement from Bonn went on: 'It should be allowed for our own as well as aircraft of Allied Forces stationed here to carry practice and dummy weapons when flying over West Germany. It is equally necessary for training purposes to practice attacks against other aircraft.'

When the subsequent Court of Inquiry published its findings the cause of the accident was clearly defined:

'The cause of the accident was the inadvertent firing of the missile by the Phantom crew who, when airborne, followed the procedures applicable to an unarmed aircraft despite carrying live weapons. It has not been established positively why the experienced and well qualified pilot forgot the real situation. It is relevant, however, that the master armament switch in the pilot's cockpit had not been taped in the safe position, which it should have been. In addition, it was found that a circuit breaker in the rear cockpit, which was normally used to isolate the firing system, was unreliable in that it was possible to depress the circuit breaker stalk just sufficiently to make electrical contact and render the circuit live, but without pushing the circuit breaker fully home.

'A further prescribed safety procedure not under the direct control of the crew also failed. The SOC are required to broadcast a "check switches safe" call during any interception by an armed aircraft. In this case, however, there was a breakdown of communications caused by a simulated exercise emergency at RAF Wildenrath and the SOC, having not been told that the Phantom was armed, did not transmit the warning call.

'The accident has been attributed to a combination of failures which together caused the prescribed safety procedures to be disregarded or rendered ineffective. However, it was determined that the ultimate responsibility for the loss of Jaguar XX963 lay with the Phantom crew.'

The incident brought about an immediate revision of regulations governing flights by armed aircraft in peacetime, as well as the introduction of a safety pin for the trigger rather than reliance on the rear cockpit circuit breaker to act as an isolating switch.

The subsequent Court Martial of the pilot and navigator — who were found guilty of negligence — was featured prominently by the daily news media which naturally made the most of the fact that a RAF jet had shot down a colleague in broad daylight.

Four months later Stephen Griggs was flying another No 14 Squadron Jaguar GR1, XX760 'AA' — the Sqn Cdr's aircraft — when he once again made a descent by courtesy of Martin-Baker. On this occasion he had been detached from Brüggen to Lossiemouth for an exercise. On the morning of 13 September he took off from the Scottish airfield leading a formation of six aircraft — one of which was also being flown by Flt Lt Paddy Mullen — to make an attack on the Tain weapons range. After successfully completing this the formation was flying over northern Scotland when the warning alarm of XX760 sounded and the No 2 engine fire warning light illuminated.

Flt Lt Griggs shut down the engine, pressed the fire extinguisher button and advised the other members of the formation that he had an engine fire warning indication. Confirmation that the rear of his aircraft was on fire was transmitted to him by a member of the formation, but when Stephen Griggs looked again at his warning panel he saw that the No 2 engine fire warning light had gone out, but all the other fire warning captions had illuminated. Further confirmation from his rear view mirror and other members of the formation that the Jaguar was still indeed on fire, left him very few options. He advised that he would eject and did so at a height of 1,200ft.

The Jaguar, still on fire, descended in a gradually steepening dive until it impacted in open moorland. Once again Stephen Griggs made an uneventful descent and was subsequently picked up by a No 202 Squadron Sea King from Lossiemouth. Investigation of the crash indicated that there had been a fracture in the combustion chamber outer casing of the No 2 engine which had allowed engine gases, at an estimated temperature of above 1,600°C, to penetrate into the engine bay in a concentrated jet. The gases had then burnt through the titanium keel structure and the floor of one of the fuselage fuel tanks. Released fuel had flowed rearwards through the engine bay and was ignited by contact with hot elements of the engine nozzles, so there was no action that Flt Lt Griggs could possibly have taken that would have saved the Jaguar.

Being shot down in peacetime by a friendly aircraft made Stephen Griggs's double ejections unique; as did the fact that on both occasions his parachute had been packed by Senior Aircraftsman (SAC) Cusak, who was naturally one of the first to receive the pilot's thanks, as well as the customary 'few' beers.

Flt Lt Mullen, who had been present on both occasions, later also ejected from a Jaguar in Oman — but that is another story.

Below:
The remains of Flt Lt Hedley Molland's Lightning F3 XP739 after his second ejection.

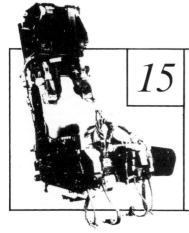

15 | It Worked As Advertised

The General Dynamics F-111 made front-page news throughout the world in April 1986 when the USAF used the latest versions of the aircraft to mount an air attack from the UK against Libya. It is unlikely that the majority reading the accounts of that action appreciated that the basic design made its first flight on 21 December 1964, served in the Vietnam War and was well used to being front-page news.

Variable geometry wings were in their infancy when the F-111A made its debut and there were many questions about the advisability of changing the angle of sweep in flight from 16° to 72.5°. Although the F-111 was not the first aircraft to employ such a controversial design, it was the first to demonstrate its practicability and the first to be put into quantity production. The aircraft survived much political and technical controversy and both the US Navy and the RAF — which had ordered 50 when the TSR2 project was cancelled — dealt body blows to General Dynamics when they cancelled their options. Although final production rates were not to achieve those originally envisaged, the F-111 was developed into a fine weapons system and electronic countermeasures aircraft and in its latest versions is a powerful weapon in the inventory of the western world.

It was not only the swing wings that caused much comment, as the aircraft included many other revolutionary features, among them being the crew escape module, which is the subject of our interest.

The unique encapsulated module designed by General Dynamics encompasses the entire cockpit area of the aircraft. In an emergency situation either the pilot or weapons systems officer (WSO), who sit side-by-side, can initiate the ejection sequence, from which point the separation from the main airframe, deployment of the drogues and capsule descent parachutes are totally automatic.

The following accounts are not only separated by five years, but also feature one of the earliest and one of the latest versions the F-111A and F-111F. It will be seen that although big steps may have been taken in the overall design of the actual aircraft, the crew escape module has remained very much as it was when it caused so much interest nearly a quarter of a century ago.

The Pilot's Story
On 4 February 1981, Capt (now Major) Barry Horne from Erwin, North Carolina, positioned his F-111F on the end of the runway at RAF Lakenheath in Suffolk. The tower had given him clearance to roll as soon as his leader was clear.

He watched the lead aircraft lift off seemingly on two tongues of flame as the afterburners of the twin Pratt & Whitney TF-30-P-100 fan-jet engines provided in excess of 25,000lb thrust each, pushing the fully-armed and fuelled aircraft into the air. Depressing his R/T switch he called 'No 2 rolling', pushed his throttles fully forward, released the brakes, and accelerated down the black strip of concrete to join his No 1.

The two F-111 crews had been briefed to carry out affiliation training over the North Sea with F-15s from Bitburg. They were carrying a mixed weapons load because their greater endurance than the F-15s would give them a much longer flight time and allow them to carry out an additional exercise once the prime objective had been accomplished. They were to rendezvous with the F-15s which were flying a Combat Air Patrol, and make a north-south run on their target to give the fighters an 'out-of-the-water' interception. During the attack run the F-111s were also to be intercepted by RAF Phantom FGR2s from Wattisham carrying out a standard air defence exercise.

The exercise went exactly to plan and after 30min the F-15s had to break off to refuel from a nearby tanker before returning to Bitburg in Germany. As they departed, the RAF Phantoms, in an agreed scenario, chased them to carry out further mock combat, before they too reached a fuel state that dictated their return to the UK.

With a maximum range of 2,500 miles on internal tanks, boosted to 3,100 miles by external tanks, the F-111Fs had no such need, so in accordance with their briefing headed north to the Darnwick Air Weapons Range to practice level, dive and toss-bomb manoeuvres. During one of these runs Barry Horne had some flight control warnings light up. In the situation the aircraft was at the time, this was not in fact unusual, and there is a set manoeuvre carried out to reset them. At this time Horne was not too concerned because after carrying out the corrective operation the lights extinguished. He therefore carried on with his planned programme, but during the toss manoeuvre the lights came on again, so he broke off, turned down-wind on the range and once again reset the warning lights. With everything once more appearing to be normal he commenced a third run, but advised his WSO that if the same situation arose, he would abort the mission and return to Lakenheath.

On the final approach into the range area, just as Barry Horne was about to start the toss manoeuvre, the dancing needles on the instrument panel were once more joined by the twinkling of the warning lights. He advised the leader that he had a problem, and was terminating the operation and returning to base. His call was acknowledged and the leader informed his No 2 that he 'was accompanying him back to the home plate in a chase position'.

The two aircraft returned at high level to Lakenheath advising the tower that the No 2 had an intermittent problem. As they approached the airfield Capt Horne suggested that the leader abandon his following position since he did not feel that he required any further assistance from him. Meanwhile, on the ground, the approach controller had alerted the emergency services and called the flying supervisor to the tower. Capt Horne exchanged information with the men on the ground and confirmed that at that time he had no further problems: he also confirmed that he had carried out his emergency checks, the lights had once again reset, and the aeroplane seemed OK for a normal landing. Approach control cleared the F-111 to descend from 3,700ft to 2,700ft, at which point Barry stabilised the aircraft and prepared to lower the landing gear ready for the final run-in. He was then cleared to descend to 1,300ft. Acknowledging this he nosed the aircraft down, but as he passed through 2,200ft noticed that the controls shuddered, causing the F-111 to pitch slightly. Within a few seconds the 'bite' he had felt disappeared and the descent continued as normal.

The flying control supervisor asked if everything was still in order but just as Barry was about to confirm there were no problems, the flight controls once again shuddered and bit, the aircraft pitched violently down and then started to roll to starboard. Moving in a reflex action he automatically applied the control inputs to correct the pitch and roll and at the same time advised the WSO that he no longer had control and to operate the ejection sequence. His brain now accelerated into overdrive, and almost in the same instant that he spoke over the R/T to the WSO, he decided not to take any chances, and also reached for the centre beam assembly where the ejection handles are located. His fingers closed around his handle and he pulled it almost in the same instant as the WSO carried out the same operation. Capt Horne recalls:

'At the time I pulled the handle the aeroplane was approximately 30° into a starboard bank with the nose 40-45° low. I can remember looking at the ground and thinking this is awfully low, as it seemed to rush up to meet me. It crossed my mind that I would not make it from this ejection. By the time I had thought that, the inertia reels had fired, I was repositioned in the cockpit and I could feel the blast from the ejection rocket nozzles pushing me away from the aeroplane, and thinking this is now a pretty good feeling. The next moment I felt the drogue and main 'chute deploy and start to slow the capsule, and the self-righting mechanism complete its operation. From the time I pulled the handle until we hit the ground I would estimate as being about 30sec. It may well have been less, as the time compression factor was certainly there although in reality things were moving pretty fast.'

The capsule landed in a softly ploughed and recently planted field at West Wraything. It was not a particularly hard landing but there was a 12kt cross-wind and before the two occupants had time to gather their wits, the module started to roll. Sensibly neither man had released his harness and they now exchanged alarmed glances. Fortunately the roll stopped before the capsule became totally inverted, but on looking out of the top of the canopy, Barry Horne saw that they were being dragged slowly towards the fireball of the aircraft some 30yd away. For the second time in the space of a few minutes, instant action was needed: without hesitation he reached for the severence handle, operated it and the parachute released immediately. Much to his relief the capsule came to an abrupt halt. He released his hatch and started to crawl out of the capsule. The WSO was a very tall and well-built man, and being in a somewhat more precarious position laying below the centre of gravity, was finding it difficult to get out of his seat, and became a little alarmed when he saw his captain disappearing. But the moment soon passed when he realised that Barry Horne was simply turning into a better position to help him.

The two crew members cleared the capsule and saw that help in the form of two local men was approaching. Noticing their hesitancy, Capt Horne and his WSO met them some 100yd from the wreckage, assured them that they were not in anyway injured and advised them to keep well clear of the burning wreckage of the aircraft. The local fire brigade were next on the scene and the fire chief showed some anxiety about explosive materials. The two airmen assured him that although the F-111 still had some small bomblets on board, there was probably more explosive material left on the capsule, so they concentrated on that. About 15min later a RAF fire team arrived, and within 30min a rescue team and engineers from the USAF base at Woodbridge added to the quickly growing crowd gathering at the scene of the accident. Neither man was injured and X-rays of the entire vertebrae system confirmed that there were no back problems. There was little damage to the capsule but in accordance with standard USAF practice — that equipment used in an aircraft accident is never re-installed in any aircraft — it was scrapped or refurbished for use as a training aid.

The WSO's Story
March 1976: The pair of F-111s from Nellis Air Force Base, Nevada, screamed low across the desert and into the Nellis practice bombing range. The lead aircraft instructed his No 2 to stand by as he pushed his machine even lower and jinked into position before laying an almost perfect bomb pattern within the target area. Clearing the range, he called the No 2 who, not to be outdone by his companion, pushed the nose of the aircraft down and started a really low-level high-speed run.

The WSO, Lt (now Major) Gary Fullington, concentrated hard on the target and was pleased with what he saw as he felt the pilot pull up to rejoin the lead aircraft. Passing 5,000ft he was aware that the aircraft appeared to have developed a will of its own. It started to buck and jink, and its actions, which observers later advised him looked as though it was trying to turn itself inside out, bore little relationship to the control inputs the pilot was applying. The nose dropped steeply to port and the tail swung violently up to starboard. Attempts were made to recover the aircraft but at 2,500ft it was clearly developing into a very marginal situation. As the wildly gyrating aircraft approached 1,800ft, the nose dipped to an angle of about 60° and swung from port to starboard as a roll developed. Finally, as the angle of roll approached 30° both men simultaneously reached for the capsule ejection handles because it was clear that the machine was now totally beyond recovery.

The escape module has two modes of operation: in the low-speed mode, the ejection rocket motor develops 2,500lb of thrust downwards and 700lb forward when the aircraft is level. In the high-speed mode it has 8,000lb downwards and 700lb rearward from the upper nozzle. The cut-off point is 300kt plus or minus 30kt. In this case the F-111 was in the low-speed envelope with the nose down, so most of thrust went downwards and pushed the capsule straight off the airframe. The two men felt that the blast was quite mild and rather different to what they had anticipated: they found themselves looking straight down at the ground which seemed — in fact was — to be rushing at them at high speed. Lt Fullington recalls thinking, 'there is no way this thing is going to stop. I'm a dead man'. But he wasn't afraid, rather feeling regret and a brief recall of all the things he had promised himself that he would do, but hadn't managed to get around to.

146

Just as it seemed that impact was inevitable, the retarding parachute, which had been deploying throughout the whole sequence, developed totally, and the capsule righted itself as the rear and front bridle cables snapped the module into a horizontal position. Calculations later indicated that this happened just 30ft off the ground! At the same moment as the capsule stabilised and both occupants breathed sighs of relief, they saw the aircraft impact on the side of a hill about 50yd above them. The exploding fireball immediately engulfed and destroyed the drogue chutes, and threatened the whole capsule. Surrounded by a ball of flame, but free of its retardation, the escape module hit the ground hard and started to roll down the hill. Both men could see the fire surrounding them, and although the impact was hard they suffered no injury — in fact in the circumstances they were in part relieved that the hillside was enabling the capsule to accelerate faster than the flames. Nevertheless Lt Fullington now felt real fear, because having appeared to recover from a seemingly too low ejection, he was now strapped inside a metal madhouse that was rolling like a roller coaster down a steep gradient. The impact had been somewhat softened by the Impact Attenuation Bag under the capsule, but fortunately for the two men this did not prevent the capsule from following its bumpy course. It bounced over several rocks, completed at least six rolls, and finally stopped inverted with the fire well behind it. The pilot and WSO were hanging upside down, both amazed that they were still in one piece.

Lt Fullington turned to his commander and said with as much calmness in his voice as he could muster, 'Are you OK?' which brought a simple nod of the head and a grin that more or less said 'Fine, but I don't want to do that again'. They gingerly unhooked themselves and carefully climbed out of the now apparently rigid capsule, wisely taking no chances because once their harnesses were open they would have been in very serious trouble if it had started to roll again. Contact with the leader, who had seen them eject and relayed a 'Mayday' call, was made on the radio stored in the survival gear. Much relieved to discover they had not been consumed in the fireball, he initiated the recovery of his two colleagues.

The accounts of the two F-111 crew members mention aspects of the capsule that should be highlighted to give an overall impression of the system. In Maj Fullington's story the rocket motor lifted the module away from the aircraft. With reference to the two modes, the break point between low and high speed is considered to be 300kt plus or minus 30kt. To select the mode, the capsule mechanism obtains the information it requires from a pitotstatic system in the aircraft, which automatically sets up the speed mode for the rocket. The safest is the slow-speed mode at low speed; while the biggest danger is low-speed mode at high speed because the parachute is deployed almost immediately in the low-speed configuration, and in high air speed situations this could result in it being ripped off by the slipstream. To help the crew there is a method of enabling the wings to be swept forward in an emergency situation when the aircraft is set up for high-speed flight. There are two large recovery parachutes fitted to the capsule, as well as a smaller drogue whose function is to stabilise the capsule at high speed and pull out the recovery parachutes at the correct time. The escape module is equipped with a barostatic control similar to that used on ejection seats, and is set for 15,000ft above mean sea level; below this the drogue is automatically severed on ejection from the aircraft.

Every capsule is fitted with a flotation bag which lessens the impact on land and supports it in water: it is in fact designed to rupture above certain impact speeds. If the capsule rolls over in water, the crew can operate two self-righting flotation bags. The port bag inflates immediately on activation and turns the capsule sideways, then 75sec later the one on the starboard side inflates to complete the self-righting feature. The capsule will float without any other buoyancy aids and is designed so that even if it half fills with water it will remain on the surface. A simple operation on board the aircraft allows both the left and right-hand control columns to be used as bilge pumps.

In the early design stages some thought was given to the capsule being fitted with a small set of stabilising wings that might be used to control it in flight, but this was abandoned so once it is separated from the main airframe its descent is controlled only by the drogues and main chutes in exactly the same way as an ejection seat. The capsule contains two complete survival kits, and in the event of an ejection over land can be used as a shelter, which gives it a distinct advantage over conventional seats!

Both Majs Horne and Fullington expressed total confidence in the escape system and were unanimous in their closing comment. 'It worked as advertised!'

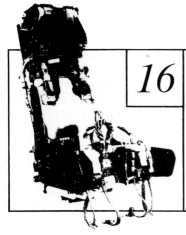

16 Nightmare In 'Nam

The clear morning sunlight danced off the silver wings and fuselage of the KC-135 tanker. Aboard the aircraft the boom operator watched the four drab-camouflaged F-105D fighter-bombers line up to replenish their fuel. He noticed that three of the aircraft had their probes extended but the fourth did not and was jinking as the pilot tried to rectify what was clearly some kind of fault. As he pondered the delay and started to wonder how it might affect the next refuelling rendezvous, the answer to his thought crackled over the intercom:

'Pontiac 4 to Pontiac Lead . . . I have a problem.'
'Pontiac Lead, go ahead Four.'
'My refuelling probe will not deploy . . . I have tried all systems but there is indication of an electrical problem.'
'Pontiac Lead. I have copied you Four. Standby.'

Pontiac 4 was flying as wing man to Capt Rick Ellis (Pontiac 3), the leader of the second element in a four-aircraft formation heading for North Vietnam to carry out an armed reconnaissance. The leader discussed the situation with Capt Ellis and it was decided that as the assignment was within what was considered to be a 'low threat area', they would take fuel and proceed as a three-aircraft formation. Pontiac Lead advised 4 of the decision and with a waggle of his wings to wish his colleagues luck, he pulled the F-105 up and peeled off on a reciprocal heading that would take him back to base. The first of the day's problems was solved, but the one Rick Ellis faced later would prove to be very much more hazardous.

It was 22 April 1966 and President Johnson had just ended the last 'bombing pause' in North Vietnam and released orders to bomb the demilitarised zone (DMZ) and areas to the north, to stem the flow of arms and troops that were adding reinforcements to the Vietcong. The aircrews in Vietnam were flying the best equipment available from the USA, and were doing everything they could to support ground forces as well as taking the fight to a relentless, resourceful, and in many cases equally well equipped enemy.

The F-105D, known among its pilots as the Thud, Led Sled or sometimes the 'Triple Threat' — a name coined in typical aircrew fashion and meaning, 'It bombed you, strafed you, then fell on you' — had first flown on 22 October 1955 and from the outset had been designed as a supersonic fighter-bomber capable of delivering a nuclear bomb from its internal weapons bay. However, circumstances

149

dictated that it became a close support strike multi-role aircraft with an external stores capacity of 12,000lb. Although it was on the verge of being phased out of service at the time of Vietnam (production ceased in 1965), it proved so effective that during the war 350 D models were refurbished and a small quantity modified to carry out an ECM role. F-105s first saw action in Vietnam in August 1964: they suffered a high loss rate mainly due to the type of operation in which they were involved, but overall were popular with pilots and their contribution to the war effort — which amounted to over 75% of all air strikes in North Vietnam — cannot be overstressed.

Rick Ellis, who now tucked into a 'V' with Pontiac Lead and Pontiac 2, was on his second tour in Vietnam flying the F-105D, and was on his 186th combat mission. During his work as a close-support pilot he had also accounted for two MiG-17s and shared in a MiG-21 with another pilot. On this occasion he was flying AF57555 which had its standard camouflage brightened by a yellow tail band and the name *Berime Imerator* (The Emperor's Warship) also in yellow, painted on the port intake.

The four aircraft took off from Takhali, Thailand at 08.30hrs. After checking in with the EC-121 AWACS, callsign 'Red Crown', they proceeded to rendezvous with the tanker before going on to seek targets to the north of Laos near the Ho Chi Minh Trail where large marshalling areas had been previously reported. After taking on fuel the formation arrived in the target zone and found what looked to be a fuel marshalling yard where between 15 and 20 trucks and 55gal drums were clearly visible. As the formation was now only three aircraft it was decided that a split attack would work well.

The leader would attack from east to west across the target, No 2 would approach from the north and pass after the leader, and Rick Ellis would follow from west to east. Each would drop three of their six 500lb GP bombs from the centre-line rack on the first pass then the lead aircraft would attack south to north, No 2 would make a run from west to east, and No 3 east to west, dropping the remaining bombs. After assessing the damage the leader would then decide whether or not to mount a further modified attack using the F-105s' 20mm M-61 cannon. The leading Thunderchief made its run according to plan and encountered no problems, No 2 screamed in low and fast and reported light to moderate ground fire, then it was the turn of Rick Ellis. As he started his run the AWACS aircraft reported it had detected MiGs approaching the area, and advised the three pilots to stay low and alert. By now No 3 was at 2,000ft approaching the target area and saw what he took to be 37mm and 100mm anti-aircraft fire coming at him from an undisclosed position north of the target approximately half a mile away. In view of this apparently increased ground activity and the imminent arrival of the MiGs, he decided to release all six bombs in one pass, then light his afterburner and head home very quickly. Just after bomb release and as he cut in the afterburner, he heard two sharp thumps from the rear of the aircraft and simultaneously saw and heard the fire warning light and annunciator. Automatically he silenced the annunciator and checked the EGT (Exhaust Gas Temperature) gauge, which was just entering the danger zone. Pulling the fire extinguisher handle he saw the warning light go out, and started to pull the F-105 into a climb. His own words describe what happened next.

'I discovered that the stick would not go beyond neutral to climb. Repeated attempts verified this and as I tried to solve the problem I called Pontiac Lead and advised him that I had been hit and had a problem. Later on I figured out that when my aircraft was hit in the aft section, a piece of shrapnel or a torn part of the aircraft had bent back and prevented the stabilator (elevator) from angling down and permitting the aircraft to climb. I looked in the rear view mirrors and saw sections of sheet metal departing the aircraft and a trail of what seemed to be white smoke. As I watched this with a certain amount of fascination, my attention was suddenly called back to the instrument panel, from where a second fire warning light now balefully stared back at me. Once again activating the extinguisher I saw that I was now down to 1,200ft and descending at what I thought was a very alarming rate. It was at this point that I decided to "punch-out". Pressing my transmit button, I advised Pontiac Lead that Pontiac 3 was "in the trees" somewhere east of the target area. I heard the leader send Pontiac 2 to 15,000ft to notify "Red Crown" that he was coming round for a position check. After setting up the ejection sequence, I was reaching for the handles when the thought of what another F-105 pilot had told me crossed my mind . . . "When you punch-out of a 'Thud' . . . you just wake up on the ground." I immediately pulled the handles and found out first hand that the axiom was true.'

Capt Ellis recovered consciousness and found himself staring down the barrels of AK47 automatic rifles, levelled at him by some very intense-looking North Vietnamese troops who were all screaming at him. Gathering his thoughts he realised that one was shouting in English, 'Get up'.

As he struggled to obey the command, an excruciating stabbing pain in both ankles made him collapse back on to the ground. Thinking that he had broken both ankles when he landed, Ellis lay in pain with the soldiers still screaming at him 'Get up, get up, get up'. He looked up at them and shouted back, 'I can't. My legs are broken'. But still they raved and gesticulated. Finally in his frustration, the pilot raised the middle finger of his right hand, but this only brought a stunning blow across his forehead from a rifle butt. The soldiers, still keeping an eye on their captive, had a discussion among themselves which culminated in one of them grabbing Ellis's right ankle and bending it through 90°, the reaction to which appeared to convince them that the pilot had injured his legs.

The policy of the Vietcong was to dispense only just enough medication to keep their prisoners alive, so when they stripped the pilot and handed him back his flight suit, they also returned his leather flying boots, the stiffness of which acted as makeshift splints for his ankles. They confiscated all his equipment including his identity tags, then told him that during his trek to captivity he would be shown to local villagers as an 'imperialist war mongering tool of the American fascists; slayer of peace-loving people's republic, baby eater, defiler of women', and so on: in general, not a 'good guy'! By this time Rick Ellis realised with considerable relief that his ankles were in fact badly sprained and not broken as he had thought.

The political officer with the patrol was Maj Tyn Ran, who ordered the construction of a 4ft square cage, into which Ellis was placed and taken to the first village east of the area into which he had ejected. Maj Ran ensured that all villagers were gathered around the cage, then made what seemed to be a long stirring political speech, ending with him leaping on to the top of the cage and urinating over the captive pilot. He then invited the villagers to throw things at the American and beat at him and the crate with sticks.

The patrol and their unfortunate captive continued eastwards for six days, averaging two stops at villages every day, where the performance of the first stop was repeated. Every other day, Ellis was given 4oz of water and pumpkin soup, a dish made from pulverised gourd which had the consistency of runny oatmeal. This was not very filling but at least marginally edible and the pilot realised that he would need to force it down if necessary so that he did not become too weak.

Soon after leaving what was the last village at which the usual 'ceremony' was undertaken, Capt Ellis was told that he was to be taken north to Hanoi for processing and further interrogation. He estimated that by this time he was approximately 50 miles inland from the sea and still fairly close to the DMZ. He was placed on a truck and taken to an area 30 miles east of the last village to await the arrival of another truckload of prisoners who were also heading north.

So far in his captivity he had been allowed out of the confines of his cage to attend to the needs of nature for about half an hour every other day. Now squatting in the cage he realised that this pause in his journey might be the last opportunity to escape. Motioning to his two guards that he needed to answer the call of nature, he was allowed to hobble to a nearby tree.

During his periods out of the cage Rick Ellis had found that the ankle sprains were improving, but he made sure that he still hobbled all the time, as his guards still believed that he was suffering from much more serious damage than he really was. Consequently by now they tended to take little notice of what he was doing, and on this occasion allowed him to go to the tree line unescorted. He went to the south side of the road and stood by a tree where the foliage was quite thick. Still the guards paid no attention and stood chatting to each other. He slowly moved to a tree a little further away, then another, all the time ready to stop if either guard looked in his direction. They did not, and gradually he moved deeper into the jungle, until he could no longer see or hear the two men. He then hurried south for 10min, west for about 15min, and north until he crossed the road he had been brought along in an easterly direction, and followed this on a ridge until he saw the truck. The two guards had by now missed him and were frantically searching the area to the south, quite convinced that no American who had escaped from their clutches would risk going north. They returned and stood by the truck, obviously discussing what action they should take. It was not long before the truck on which he had been destined to be taken north arrived. The troops manning it exchanged a few heated words with the two original guards, who eventually handed them something and each departed in separate directions. Rick Ellis later discovered that they had given the new arrivals his identity discs (dog tags) telling them that they had shot the American because he tried to escape. This information was passed by the North Vietnamese to the International Red Cross, who in turn informed the USAF who told his parents that their son had been killed in action (KIA).

After the trucks left, the pilot stayed under cover until he could no longer hear any sounds of them, then crossed the road and headed south until dusk.

His jungle survival training now became vital, but without any form of survival equipment he had to rely on what he could find to eat and drink as he tried to get back to the American lines. The environment was extremely hostile to those unprepared to fight it, so in just a flight suit and boots, the dangers he had to contend with can be imagined. The intense heat during the day was strength-sapping, and for six days Ellis had been deprived of a balanced diet.

In addition he also had to be wary of the wild life, especially snakes. The aircrew called the dangerous snakes one or two steppers, depending on how many steps could be taken after they had struck. There was also a king cobra-type snake, some of which had been reported as being 25ft long, referred to as 'no-steppers' for they knocked their victim down and killed instantly. But the most feared was the krait which was the size of a garden worm used for fishing and whose bite was instantly fatal. Against these the escaped pilot had no protection other than his stout boots.

For four days he overcame every problem, eating what he knew to be safe and leaving any berries or other roots that he suspected; but progressively he became more ill and by the fifth day was very weak. After sleeping fitfully, he found some water and started off once more heading south. As he stumbled along, a sound caught his attention: he stopped and listened, and above the sounds of the jungle he heard a familiar throb. It grew louder, and he knew it was a helicopter.

Carefully moving to the edge of a nearby clearing, he saw a Marine Huey gunship which was checking the area for infiltrators. He was overjoyed because he knew instantly that he had passed through the DMZ and was in South Vietnam. Running from cover he waved at the Huey and saw that one of the gunners had seen him, but was horrified to see the man swing his M-60 machine gun towards him. He thought, 'Boy this is great, I spend all this effort getting away from the north, and I'm going to be "hosed" by my own guys'. Fortunately the gunner did not fire and the helicopter started to circle the waving figure.

Calling on unknown depths of energy, Rick Ellis kept running, waving his arms and shouting, not realising that above the noise of the thrashing rotors the crew could not hear him anyway. Finally he fell delirious and exhausted, but struggled to his knees in a last despairing effort, and saw that the Huey was landing. Two Marines with side arms aimed at the gesticulating figure, cautiously approached as he fell over again, then he felt them pick him up and one shouted, 'Christ. You're an American.' Carefully they took him aboard the helicopter which was still hovering just above the ground with those on board half expecting some form of ambush. When they too saw his flight suit and heard his delirious mutterings, they had no doubt as to their 'find'.

The helicopter pilot lifted his aircraft clear and headed for a Forward Operations Base, from where Capt Ellis was medivac'ed to the USS *Oriskinsy* and then to Clark AFB in the Philippines, and back to the States. Little of this was clear to him at the time as he was still dangerously weak, delirious and heavily sedated. But he did manage to arrange for four cases of whisky to be sent to the crew of the Huey, and found out later that these did reach them.

Capt Ellis spent three months in hospital after which he returned to active duty as a Major flying F-105s on assignment as a weapons instructor for his final 15 months of service. He owes his life not only to the Republic seat fitted to the aircraft but also to his own fortitude, training and skill in jungle survival in coming through what had been briefed as an operation in a fairly safe area, but turned into a nightmare.

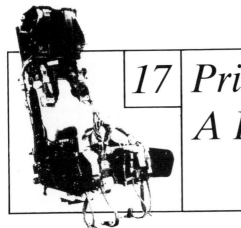

17 *Prisoner On A Pillion*

Troops of Compania de Commandos 601, an Argentine Special Forces unit deployed at Port Howard on the east coast of the West Falklands, were expecting trouble. It was 21 May 1982 and a lone Harrier GR3 of the RAF had screamed across their positions obviously carrying out a reconnaissance which could mean that an attack from the sea or air was imminent. On this occasion no attempt had been made to intercept the aircraft which would have perhaps exposed the disposition of their forces to the Harrier's pilot. They prepared themselves for what was to come and 15min later were a little surprised when they received warning that what seemed to be another singleton was approaching their position, albeit from a different direction, for it was fairly unusual for the British to make two reconnaissance runs over the same area so close together.

The Argentinians at Port Howard had no way of knowing that the aircraft was in fact the same one. The Harrier appeared, travelling low and very fast, but this time it would not have the sky to itself. As it neared Packe's Port it came within range of British-manufactured Blowpipe SAMs. One of the soldiers fired at the enemy aircraft which almost immediately started to roll as it was hit. Watchers saw two parts detach themselves as the Harrier rolled violently and crashed to earth: one was half the starboard wing, and the other was the pilot who ejected and was seen to plummet into the sea trailing a partly deployed parachute. The Argentinians were jubilant at their success but immediately launched a boat to mount a rescue attempt of the downed airman.

In 1940, RAF pilots had flown Gladiators off the deck of HMS *Glorious* during the defence of Norway, and later had also volunteered to fly Hurricanes and Gladiators back on board. This was no mean feat when the full implication of deck landings with the need to catch arrestor wires is considered, especially as the pilots concerned had received no training. Similarly, in 1942 Spitfires and Hurricanes had been flown off the heaving decks of British and American carriers in the Mediterranean to bring relief to the besieged island of Malta. On such occasions the pilots were using the carriers either as a way of recovering much needed aircraft, in the case of the Norwegian campaign, or in the Mediterranean Sea as stepping stones bringing Malta's runways into range. In the strictest sense the RAF pilots had not been using the carriers as operational bases from which to mount a complete start-to-finish operation. In the case of the 1982 Falklands campaign the unique handling qualities of the V/STOL Harrier had enabled RAF pilots who were used to operating from land bases, to support the Royal Navy's

Fleet Air Arm from carriers with a minimum amount of training in deck-landing techniques. The ability of the Harrier to leave the carrier in practically any situation, without it being necessary for it to always steam into wind, also gave the Task Force Commander an advantage that would have been the envy of his World War 2 counterpart.

No 1(F) Squadron of the RAF had been alerted on 8 April 1982 to prepare for carrier operations in the South Atlantic, their GR3s being necessary to support the task force carriers' Sea Harriers. The first deployment to Ascension Island comprised six aircraft which were taken aboard the ill-fated *Atlantic Conveyor* off Ascension on 6 May. The Harriers landed on a specially constructed pad and parked on the deck between other stores. The Royal Navy's Sea Harrier FRS1s had been designed from the outset to operate in hostile environments associated with maritime operations, whereas the GR3 versions of the RAF had many parts that would be damaged by salt spray. So it was necessary to treat the aircraft and engines with corrosive protection sprays and materials. Pilots and groundcrews for the RAF aircraft were taken on board with the Harriers, although some travelled south on the *Norland*. On 18 May four of the six Harriers were flown from the *Conveyor* to HMS *Hermes*, the first of these, XZ972, in the hands of the commanding officer of No 1(F) Squadron, Wg Cdr (now Group Captain) Peter Squire.

Three days later it was XZ972, this time being flown by Flt Lt (now Squadron Leader) Jeff Glover, that was shot down by the SAM. Wg Cdr Squire and Flt Lt Glover had been briefed to provide close air support in and around the San Carlos area, where the British were conducting their landings. The two Harriers left the carrier in CAVU (Ceiling and Visibility Unlimited) conditions, the sun shining quite strongly but not adding a great deal of heat to the day. Almost immediately the pair encountered problems when Peter Squire was unable to raise the undercarriage of his aircraft. He had no choice other than to return to the carrier and left Jeff Glover to continue as a singleton. The lone Harrier was directed towards the San Carlos area but there appeared to be no targets for his cluster bombs so he was then tasked to Port Howard and on arrival made a low-level run from south to north. Reporting that he had been unable to locate any targets, he was directed to hold at 10,000ft some 20 miles away to the north and await further instructions. About 15min later the Tasker asked him to make another run which he did, this time approaching from the west.

Flashing across the landscape with his port-facing camera operating he was approaching Port Howard at an IAS of 510kt at about 150-200ft and was rolling out of a turn when he heard and felt three bangs in fairly quick succession. At the time he was concentrating on ground features but recalls that his airspeed was as reported although the height was purely a visual assessment. At the time of the hits (which Jeff Glover recounts as sounding Bang! . . . Bang! Bang!) he was over the water just about to close in on Port Howard village. As soon as the Harrier started to roll, he instinctively attempted corrective action by pushing the stick to port, but it would not move and he at once realised that he had no control whatsoever. At this point everything seemed to slow down: he recalls seeing the sea where sky should have been, and the whole landscape revolving around his cockpit. He looked down towards the firing handle of the Mk 9 Martin-Baker seat located between his legs, then glancing up saw he was inverted and quickly realised that if he ejected in this position he would go straight into the sea. Therefore he calculated that by delaying the firing sequence until the aircraft was nearly through its rolling circle, he should leave it in the right plane. Although the rate of roll was approaching 360° per sec, it seemed an age before he was in the position he knew to be best for the ejection.

(This is a situation that has been commented on by many aircrew to whom the author spoke during research, including a Canberra pilot who was faced with an almost identical problem to that of Jeff Glover. In his case he counted in his mind the degrees through which he passed and ordered his two crew members to eject on his command. As the gyrating Canberra approached the normal upright position he called. 'Eject! Eject!' then followed when he heard the crack of their seats' cartridges. But he, like many of the others, had much more height than the Harrier pilot.)

Let Jeff Glover continue his story:

'I looked down and saw my right hand on the ejection handle and pulling it, so I was obviously not in an ideal ejection posture. The other thing that wasn't right, was that my left hand should have been on my right wrist as I pulled the handle. But it wasn't. It was still on the throttle in the top left-hand corner of the cockpit as I still had full power applied to the engine. So as I went out my head was down, and my left hand was out of position. I heard an initial crack which I presume was the miniature detonating cord shattering the canopy, followed by a sort of metallic-type ring. I am not too sure what that was but think it may have been the primary cartridge on the ejection gun. After that I remember nothing because I blacked out.'

As he left the Harrier he hit a 600mph slipstream which whipped his left arm back, breaking it very close to the top. His collar bone and shoulder blade were also broken, the latter being the most painful for although it is a fairly thin bone it is protected by a lot of muscle and apparently takes something akin to a good hit by a hammer to fracture it. Clearly the speed of the slipstream on this occasion was more than adequate to simulate such a domestic tool! Under the circumstances it is not surprising that he lost consciousness, only recovering after automatic separation had occurred and finding himself about 6ft under the sea, swallowing water like mad. Jeff saw that in one direction it appeared to be light and in another total darkness, so he kicked out for the light area and soon surfaced in the bay near Port Howard. His immediate thought was 'I'm alive. Thank God'.

This was followed by a moment of panic when he realised that he was blind in his left eye, as well as being in some considerable pain from his shoulder and back. There was also a lot of blood in his right eye and on his face. His helmet and mask were missing, but the oxygen hose was hanging from the clip on his Mae West (life jacket), and it seems likely that it was the metal clip at the top of the hose that cut his face when it became detached as the helmet and mask were torn away during the ejection sequence.

He was clearly in a state of *non compos mentis* because he did not think to inflate his life jacket and it was only the buoyancy of his immersion suit that was keeping him afloat. He recalls that he thought his dinghy pack was still suspended beneath him on its attachment lanyard, but a photograph later sent to him by one of his rescuers shows it inflated.

Jeff Glover was clearly suffering from shock but at the same time he was elated at having survived the ejection and was pondering his position when he heard voices. Looking around he saw they came from Argentinian soldiers on board an approaching rowing boat. They gently pulled him aboard together with the dinghy, and headed towards the beach, and for him captivity. On reaching the shore he saw that the reception party included a man astride a motor cycle, and was a little surprised when he identified himself as 'Capitano — Commando — Medico', which was like music to his ears as he realised that he was some form of medical officer. The Argentinians indicated to the pilot that he was to get on the pillion of the motorcycle, which he did, and with two soldiers running alongside, was taken to a building outside of which there was a sign indicating that it was the Port Howard Social Club. It was in fact being used as a field hospital. Once inside Jeff Glover had his wet clothing removed and handed his captors his Geneva ID Card which he had inside his immersion suit. The doctor cleaned the blood away from his face, then inserted a couple of stitches in the cut above his lip, after which he was given a shot from a hypodermic needle. Drowsiness and sleep quickly followed and it was to be 10-12hr later before he awoke.

In addition to the injuries mentioned it was also found that he had some small compression fractures in the lower back, and at the top of his spine by the base of his neck.

On 22 May he was flown to Goose Green by helicopter and from there to Port Stanley from where the next night a C-130 of Grupo 1 flew him to Comodoro Rivadavia on the mainland. He was reasonably well looked after by the Argentinians and after 7½ weeks in captivity was released on 8 July 1982, returning to England with the distinction of being the only RAF PoW of the Falklands campaign.

On return to England he spent three months at RAF Hedley Court and one month at the RAF Hospital at Wroughton. He was cleared by the doctors for flying in January 1983 and returned to No 1(F) Squadron at Wittering to continue where he had left off in May 1982.

Now totally recovered, Sqn Ldr Glover is with the Red Arrows. Like many aircrew he will concede that the ejection seat is not perhaps the most relaxing item to be strapped to for prolonged periods, but he is ready to admit that on 21 May 1982 when his Harrier started acting like a catherine wheel, it was the most comfortable seat he had ever experienced — although a motorcycle pillion runs it a close second!

Left:
Flt Lt Jeff Glover in the cockpit of a No 1(F) Squadron Harrier GR3 after his return from the Falklands. *Sqn Ldr Glover*

Above:
Wg Cdr Peter Squire, CO of No 1(F) Squadron, landing Harrier GR3 XV992 on HMS *Hermes* during the Falklands campaign. *BAe*

Below:
Jeff Glover being recovered from the sea by Argentinian soldiers. His dinghy, which he could not recall inflating, can be seen in the back of the row boat. *Sqn Ldr Glover*

160